Baldee

Y0-BZV-400

HOSPITALITY FINANCIAL ACCOUNTING WORKBOOK

Lead Author

Neville Joffe

Contributors and Reviewers

Bharat Aggarwal, BBA, MBA, CMA
Sheridan College

Jason Armstrong, CPA, CGA
Fanshawe College

Maria Belanger, CPA, CA
Algonquin College

Ben Carnovale, BBA, MASc
Confederation College

Dave Hummel, CPA, CA
Conestoga College

Laurette Korman, MBA, CMA
Kwantlen Polytechnic University

Annamaria Kougias, B.Ed
Centennial College

Chris Leduc, CPA, CA
Cambrian College

Kayla Levesque, CPA, CA
Cambrian College

Rachel McCorriston, CPA, CMA, MBA
Fanshawe College

Susan Rogers, CPA, CMA
Sheridan College

AME | Learning

Textbook ISBN: 978-1-926751-53-5
Workbook ISBN: 978-1-926751-54-2

Hospitality Financial Accounting
Author: Neville Joffe
Publisher: AME Learning Inc.
Content Contributors and Developmental Editors:
Kobboon Chotruangprasert/Graeme Gomes/Kyle Kroetsch
Production Editors: Joshua Peters/Melody Yousefian
Copy Editor: Nicola Balfour
Indexer: Elizabeth Walker
Typesetter: Paragon Prepress Inc.
Vice President and Publishing Manager: Linda Zhang
Cover Design: Sasha Moroz/Bram Wigzell
Online Course Design & Production: AME Multimedia Team

4 5 Webcom 20 19

For more information contact:

AME Learning Inc.
410-1220 Sheppard Avenue East
Toronto, ON, Canada M2K 2S5
Phone: 416.479.0200
Toll-free: 1.888.401.3881
E-mail: info@amelearning.com
Visit our website at: www.amelearning.com

Table of Contents

Chapter 1

FINANCIAL STATEMENTS: PERSONAL ACCOUNTING

LEARNING OUTCOMES

❶ Describe the purpose of accounting

❷ Describe the balance sheet and the income statement

❸ Define an accounting period

❹ Explain how the accounting equation works

❺ Explain accrual-based accounting

❻ Explain how to account for debt and assets

❼ Explain how to account for prepaid expenses

❽ Distinguish between capital and revenue

❾ Demonstrate how double entries are recorded in T-accounts

AMEENGAGE *Access* ***ameengage.com*** *for integrated resources including tutorials, practice exercises, the digital textbook and more.*

Assessment Questions

AS-1 (❶)

Define accounting and describe the purpose of accounting.

____

____

____

AS-2 (❷)

What is net worth?

____

____

AS-3 (❷)

In simple terms, what are assets and liabilities?

____

____

AS-4 (❷)

What are revenues and expenses?

AS-5 (❷)

Explain the role of the balance sheet.

AS-6 (❷)

Explain the role of the income statement.

AS-7 (❸)

What are some advantages of using monthly accounting periods in your personal balance sheet?

AS-8 (❹)

What is the accounting equation?

AS-9 (❽)

What is the equation for calculating ending net worth for a period?

AS-10 (❷)

Define surplus and deficit.

AS-11 (❹)

What is a T-account?

AS-12 (❺)

Explain accrual-based accounting.

AS-13 (❺)

Briefly describe the cash-based method of accounting.

____

____

AS-14 (❻)

True or False: When you borrow money, you have more cash but your net worth decreases.

____

AS-15 (❻)

True or False: When you pay off a loan, your cash decreases and your net worth increases.

____

____

AS-16 (❻)

True or False: Buying an asset has no impact on net worth.

____

AS-17 (❼)

What is a prepaid expense?

____

____

AS-18 (❼)

When an expense is initially prepaid, which accounts increase or decrease?

____

____

AS-19 (❼)

When does an expense need to be recorded under accrual-based accounting? What are the three possible timings the payment can be made for an expense?

AS-20 (❽)

What is capital?

Application Questions Group A

AP-1A (❷)

April Rose had the following financial data for the year ended December 31, 2016

Cash	$6,000
Jewellery	10,000
Automobile	18,000
House	256,000
Bank Loan	45,000
Credit Card	5,000
Mortgage	140,000

Required

a) Calculate April Rose's total assets.

Assets 290,000

Liabi

b) Calculate April Rose's total liabilities.

190,000

NW = 100,000

AP-2A (❷ ❹)

Consider the following information for Julius Troy

Cash	$12,000
Jewellery	18,000
Automobile	22,000
House	161,000
Credit Card	5,000
Bank Loan	10,000
Mortgage	125,000

Required

a) Calculate Julius Troy's total assets.

213,000

b) Calculate Julius Troy's total liabilities.

140,000

c) Calculate Julius Troy's net worth.

73,000

AP-3A (❻)

Darryl purchased a new laptop on January 1, 2016 worth $2,000. He paid the entire amount using cash. He also purchased a new cell phone worth $300 on account. How will these transactions affect Darryl's net worth?

AP-4A (❷ ❺ ❽ ❾)

The following information was taken from the personal records of Juliet Lahm on April 30, 2016

Cash	$3,000
Jewellery	2,000
House	190,000
Mortgage	80,000
Net Worth	115,000

Transactions for the month of May 2016

1. Earned monthly salary of $5,050.
2. Paid $1,200 cash for utilities.
3. Purchased an automobile worth $10,000 on account.
4. Paid $600 cash for food expenses.
5. Paid $400 cash for gas.

Required

a) Complete the Cash T-account to determine the ending balance of cash.

INCREASE +	CASH	DECREASE −
Opening Bal.		

b) Complete the personal income statement to determine the surplus or deficit for the period.

Personal Income Statement For the Month Ended May 31, 2016		

c) What is Juliet Lahm's net worth on May 31?

____

____

____

AP-5A (❷ ❹)

A person has the following information with regard to his own balance sheet, but the liability section is missing.

Cash	$35,000
Automobile	58,000
House	100,000
Net Worth	55,000

Required

Determine the total amount of liabilities.

____

____

____

____

AP-6A (❹)

Calculate the missing amounts in the following table.

	Scenario 1	Scenario 2
Total Assets	$123,000	
Total Liabilities		$34,000
Net Worth	$94,000	$114,000

AP-7A (❹)

As of December 31, 2015, Maria Green had total assets of $40,000, and total liabilities of $15,000. As of December 31, 2016, Maria's total assets and liabilities increased to $50,000 and $30,000, respectively. How has Maria's net worth changed since the end of 2015?

____

____

____

____

AP-8A (❷ ❹ ❾)

The following information pertains to Ken White's personal financial transactions

Opening Balances as at January 1, 2016	
Cash	$9,000
Contents of Home	6,000
Automobile	29,000
House	156,000
Unpaid Accounts	5,500
Bank Loan	60,000
Net Worth	134,500

Transactions for the month of January 2016

1. Paid maintenance expense for the month of January with $120 cash.
2. Purchased new furniture worth $2,500 with cash.
3. Paid credit card liability of $5,500 (Unpaid Accounts) in full.
4. Paid telephone, electricity and water bill for January with $1,200 cash.
5. Purchased $2,000 of groceries and goods for personal consumption with cash.
6. Deposited $4,040 salary earned during the month.

Required

a) Using the information provided, record the opening balances in the T-accounts.

b) Record the transactions for the month of January in the T-accounts.

PERSONAL BALANCE SHEET
As at January 31, 2016

ASSETS

INCREASE | DECREASE
+ **CASH** -
Opening

INCREASE | DECREASE
+ **CONTENTS OF HOME** -
Opening

INCREASE | DECREASE
+ **AUTOMOBILE** -
Opening

INCREASE | DECREASE
+ **HOUSE** -
Opening

LIABILITIES

DECREASE | INCREASE
- **UNPAID ACCOUNTS** +
Opening

DECREASE | INCREASE
- **BANK LOAN** +
Opening

NET WORTH

DECREASE | INCREASE
- **NET WORTH** +
Opening

TOTAL ASSETS ______
TOTAL LIABILITIES ______
NET WORTH ______ } ______

PERSONAL INCOME STATEMENT
For the Month Ended Jan. 31, 2016

DECREASE | INCREASE
- **REVENUE** +

LESS EXPENSES

INCREASE | DECREASE
+ **ENTERTAINMENT EXPENSE** -

INCREASE | DECREASE
+ **FOOD EXPENSE** -

INCREASE | DECREASE
+ **INTEREST EXPENSE** -

INCREASE | DECREASE
+ **MAINTENANCE EXPENSE** -

INCREASE | DECREASE
+ **UTILITIES EXPENSE** -

TOTAL REVENUE ______
LESS TOTAL EXPENSES ______
SURPLUS (DEFICIT) ______

AP-9A (❷ ❹ ❾)

Alan Marshall is preparing his balance sheet and income statement for the month ended April 30, 2016. Use the following information to help him prepare his financial statements.

Opening Balances as at April 1, 2016	
Cash	$5,000
Contents of Home	1,000
Automobile	4,000
House	280,000
Unpaid Accounts	10,000
Auto Loan	30,000
Net Worth	250,000

Transactions for the month of April

1. Purchased new furniture worth $2,000 for home using credit card.
2. Paid credit card bill with $3,000 cash.
3. Paid utility bills of $800 for the month of April using credit card.
4. Purchased groceries and food for $2,500 using cash.
5. Made a principal payment of $1,250 for the auto loan.
6. Paid April's rent of $1,500 with cash.
7. Deposited $4,050 salary earned during the month.

Required

a) Using the information provided, record the opening balances in the T-accounts.

b) Record the transactions for the month of April in the T-accounts.

PERSONAL BALANCE SHEET
As at April 30, 2016

ASSETS

INCREASE DECREASE
+ **CASH** -
Opening

INCREASE DECREASE
+ **CONTENTS OF HOME** -
Opening

INCREASE DECREASE
+ **AUTOMOBILE** -
Opening

INCREASE DECREASE
+ **HOUSE** -
Opening

LIABILITIES

DECREASE INCREASE
- **UNPAID ACCOUNTS** +
Opening

DECREASE INCREASE
- **AUTO LOAN** +
Opening

NET WORTH

DECREASE INCREASE
- **NET WORTH** +
Opening

TOTAL ASSETS ______

TOTAL LIABILITIES ______

NET WORTH ______

PERSONAL INCOME STATEMENT
For the Month Ended April 30, 2016

DECREASE INCREASE
- **REVENUE** +

LESS EXPENSES

INCREASE DECREASE
+ **ENTERTAINMENT EXPENSE** -

INCREASE DECREASE
+ **FOOD EXPENSE** -

INCREASE DECREASE
+ **INTEREST EXPENSE** -

INCREASE DECREASE
+ **MAINTENANCE EXPENSE** -

INCREASE DECREASE
+ **RENT EXPENSE** -

INCREASE DECREASE
+ **UTILITIES EXPENSE** -

TOTAL REVENUE ______

LESS TOTAL EXPENSES ______

SURPLUS (DEFICIT) ______

AP-10A (❷ ❸)

John Black is a senior administrator at a market research firm, and recently received a salary increase from $3,500 per month to $4,000 per month. He feels richer and would like to know the increase in his net worth. However, he has never prepared a personal balance sheet or an income statement that would help him understand his net worth. John gathered the following information to help him understand his financial position.

	September 30, 2016	October 31, 2016	November 30, 2016
Cash	$1,000	$2,150	$4,050
House	120,000	120,000	120,000
Bank Loan	400	350	300
Salary	3,500	3,500	4,000
Entertainment Expense	200	500	400
Food Expense	1,500	1,200	1,100
Insurance Expense	150	150	150
Utilities Expense	200	400	300
Miscellaneous Expense	175	50	100

Required

Prepare John Black's income statement for the three months.

John Black Personal Income Statement For the Month Ending				
	September 30, 2016	October 31, 2016	November 30, 2016	Total

AP-11A (❸ ❽)

Jeff Winger is working at a law firm. His salary recently increased and he would like to keep track of his net worth. Jeff has gathered the following information to help you track his net worth. Assume the opening net worth for June 30 is $0.

	June 30, 2016	July 31, 2016	August 31, 2016
Cash	$2,500	$4,100	$6,300
Automobile	13,000	13,000	13,000
Credit Card Bills	1,000	800	500
Automobile Loan	12,000	11,500	11,000
Salary	4,300	4,900	4,900
Food Expense	290	500	100
Entertainment Expense	210	800	500
Rent Expense	1,300	1,300	1,300

Complete the table below.

	June 30, 2016	July 31, 2016	August 31, 2016
Opening Net Worth			
Surplus (Deficit)			
Closing Net Worth			

Analysis

After looking at the table you prepared for Jeff, he notices that his cash has not increased by as much as his net worth has. Why is this the case?

AP-12A (❷ ❹)

Using the opening balances provided in the balance sheets below, enter the updated amounts for each transaction in the blank balance sheets labelled Answers.

1. Borrowed $4,000 from the bank.

Opening Balances

Assets		Liabilities	
Cash	$5,000	Unpaid Accounts	$3,000
Investment	8,000	Bank Loan	0
Contents of Home	6,000	Automobile Loan	5,000
Automobile	20,000	Student Loan	6,000
House	280,000	Mortgage	250,000
		Total Liabilities	264,000
		Net Worth	55,000
Total Assets	$319,000	**Total Liabilities + Net Worth**	$319,000

Answers

2. Purchased $3,000 of investments in cash.

Opening Balances

Assets		**Liabilities**	
Cash	$7,000	Unpaid Accounts	$3,000
Investment	8,000	Bank Loan	0
Contents of Home	6,000	Automobile Loan	5,000
Automobile	20,000	Student Loan	6,000
House	180,000	Mortgage	150,000
		Total Liabilities	164,000
		Net Worth	57,000
Total Assets	$221,000	**Total Liabilities + Net Worth**	$221,000

Answers

3. Paid $1,000 to reduce an outstanding automobile loan (principal portion).

Opening Balances

Assets		**Liabilities**	
Cash	$3,000	Unpaid Accounts	$3,000
Contents of Home	6,000	Bank Loan	0
Automobile	20,000	Automobile Loan	5,000
House	180,000	Student Loan	6,000
		Mortgage	150,000
		Total Liabilities	164,000
		Net Worth	45,000
Total Assets	$209,000	**Total Liabilities + Net Worth**	$209,000

Answers

4. Bought a motorcycle for $6,000. Paid a $1,000 deposit with cash and borrowed $5,000 from the bank.

Opening Balances

Assets		**Liabilities**	
Cash	$2,000	Unpaid Accounts	$3,000
Contents of Home	4,000	Bank Loan	1,000
Motorcycle	0	Student Loan	11,000
Automobile	20,000	Mortgage	150,000
House	180,000	**Total Liabilities**	165,000
		Net Worth	41,000
Total Assets	$206,000	**Total Liabilities + Net Worth**	$206,000

Answers

AP-13A (❸)

John Hollister collected the following amounts in cash for the month of February 2016

Salary paid by employer	$2,400
Winnings at the casino	$270
Gifts	$295
Performance bonus paid by employer	$450

Required

Calculate John's total revenue and total capital items for February 2016.

____

____

____

AP-14A (❹)

Indicate whether the terms of the accounting equation will increase, decrease or stay the same for each transaction by placing a "+" or "–" in the appropriate space. If an item is not changed by the transaction, leave the space blank. The first transaction has been completed for you.

Transaction	Assets	= Liabilities	+ Net Worth
Deposited salary earned.	+		+
1. Purchased a new TV on credit.			
2. Received a cash gift.			
3. Purchased fuel for car on credit.			
4. Made a loan payment including interest.			
5. Received cash from a student loan.			
6. Received a paycheque.			

AP-15A (❷ ❺ ❾)

The following information is available from Anna Edison's financial records

Opening Balances as at June 1, 2016	
Cash	$18,000
Furniture	3,100
Valuables & Electronics	3,200
House	255,000
Student Loans	39,000
Family Loan	2,000
Mortgage	100,000
Net Worth	138,300

The following transactions took place during the month of June

1. $350 was taken from the bank account for a car lease payment.
2. Paid $1,000 cash against the student loans. Includes $140 of interest.
3. Won a tablet worth $800 as a raffle prize.
4. Made a mortgage payment of $2,000 with cash. Includes $400 interest.
5. $4,800 salary earned was directly deposited to the bank account.
6. Family member accepted jewellery of $2,000 in repayment of the loan.

a) Record the transactions in the T-accounts.

PERSONAL BALANCE SHEET
As at June 30, 2016

ASSETS

Increase | Decrease
+ **CASH** -
Opening

Increase | Decrease
+ **FURNITURE** -
Opening

Increase | Decrease
+ **VALUABLES & ELECTRONICS** -
Opening

Increase | Decrease
+ **HOUSE** -
Opening

LIABILITIES

Decrease | Increase
- **STUDENT LOANS** +
Opening

Decrease | Increase
- **FAMILY LOAN** +
Opening

Decrease | Increase
- **MORTGAGE** +
Opening

Decrease | Increase
- **NET WORTH** +
Opening

Total Assets ______

Total Liabilities ______ } ______

Net Worth ______

INCOME STATEMENT
For the Month Ended June 30, 2016

REVENUE

Decrease | Increase
- | +

LESS EXPENSES

Increase | Decrease
+ **AUTOMOBILE EXPENSE** -

Increase | Decrease
+ **ENTERTAINMENT EXPENSE** -

Increase | Decrease
+ **GROCERIES EXPENSE** -

Increase | Decrease
+ **INTEREST EXPENSE** -

Increase | Decrease
+ **TRAVEL EXPENSE** -

Total Revenue ______

Less Total Expenses ______

Surplus (Deficit) ______

b) Complete the income statement and balance sheet.

Income Statement For the Month Ended June 30, 2016		

Personal Balance Sheet As at June 30, 2016			

AP-16A (❹ ❾)

Indicate whether assets, liabilities or net worth will increase or decrease and by how much, based on each transaction. The first one has been done for you. Always ensure the accounting equation is balanced.

Provide an explanation only if net worth is affected.

	Assets	= Liabilities	+ Net Worth	Explanation
1. Purchased a new television for $700 on credit.	+700	+700		
2. Received $2,000 salary.				
3. Paid $1,200 cash for one year of insurance.				
4. Purchased a new $500 gaming console with cash.				
5. Paid for groceries with $80 cash.				
6. Paid $400 toward the car loan.				
7. Paid $30 interest on the car loan.				
8. Paid $600 toward unpaid bills.				
9. Used one month of insurance.				

AP-17A (❹ ❼ ❾)

Indicate whether the account balances will increase or decrease and by how much, based on each transaction. The first one has been done for you. Always ensure the accounting equation is balanced.

	Assets =	Liabilities +	Net Worth	Explanation
1. Purchased a new television for $700 on credit.	+ 700	+ 700		
2. Purchased $100 worth of gas on credit.				
3. Made a $850 car loan payment.				
4. Purchased a chandelier for $200 cash.				
5. Prepaid three months of rent with $3,300 cash.				
6. Received a cash gift of $500.				
7. Used up one of three months of prepaid rent.				
8. Paid interest of $50, in cash, on the car loan.				
9. Received a phone bill for $110.				

Analysis

The net worth account is only updated at the end of an accounting period. Revenue and expense accounts, and the net worth account, track changes in net worth during the period. For each transaction that affects net worth, determine whether a revenue, expense, or net worth is used to track the change.

AP-18A (❷ ❹ ❼)

On December 1, 2016, Shervin decided to track his finances. On this date, his assets and liabilities were

Cash	$14,000
Prepaid Rent	3,000
Prepaid Insurance	300
House	160,000
Contents of Home	19,000
Automobile	30,000
Student Loan	10,000
Unpaid Accounts	17,000
Bank Loan	25,000
Mortgage	120,000

Required

a) What is the value of his total assets?

____

____

____

____

b) What is the value of his total liabilities?

____

____

____

c) What is Shervin's net worth on December 1, 2016?

____

____

d) During the month of December, Shervin recognized $150 of prepaid expenses as an actual expense on the income statement. Calculate the change in his cash account and net worth.

Transaction	Cash	Net Worth
Effect		

AP-19A (❹ ❻)

Nick Miller wrote down his personal accounting information but some of it was destroyed.

Bicycle	$700
Automobile	3,000
Cash	800
Furniture	?
Net Worth	3,350
Overdue Rent	?
Television	500
Total Assets	6,100
Unpaid Bills	2,300

Required

a) How much is Nick's furniture worth?

b) How much rent does Nick owe?

Analysis

Nick has worked 80 hours at his job as a bartender and earned $1,900 but will not get paid for another two weeks. According to accrual-based accounting has Nick's net worth increased? Why or why not?

AP-20A (❹)

State how the following transactions would affect net worth (increase, decrease, no change)

Transaction	Effect on Net Worth
Borrow cash.	
Pay entertainment expense with cash.	
Pay food expense with cash.	
Buy assets with cash.	
Charge home repairs expense on credit card.	
Pay insurance expense with cash.	
Pay loan principal with cash.	
Purchase assets on account.	
Receive salary.	
Pay rent expense with cash.	

AP-21A (❷ ❺)

Using the following chart, indicate whether there would be an increase, decrease or no change to cash and net worth for the transactions provided. The first transaction has been completed for you.

		Cash			Net Worth		
	Transaction	Increase	Decrease	No Change	Increase	Decrease	No Change
1	Deposit salary earned.	X			X		
2	Pay cash for food.						
3	Purchase a new car.						
4	Pay rent expense in advance.						
5	Reduce student loan principal.						
6	Buy a new computer with cash.						
7	Obtain a bank loan.						
8	Pay entertainment expenses.						
9	Record cash earned from a part-time job.						

AP-22A (8)

Joana Harwin collected the following amounts in cash for the month of March 2016

Full-time employment income	$1,200
Income from part-time babysitting job	$220
Rental income	$525

Required

Calculate Joana's total revenue and total capital items for March 2016.

___

___

___

Application Questions Group B

AP-1B (❷)

Dana Shukrun was reviewing her records on December 31, 2016. Below is a list of items and their value.

Cash	$7,900
Computer	700
Automobile	19,100
House	255,000
Mortgage	150,000
Credit Card	4,600
Bank Loan	37,700

Required

a) Calculate Dana Shukrun's total assets.

____

____

b) Calculate Dana Shukrun's total liabilities.

____

____

AP-2B (❷ ❹)

John Bonham was performing a year-end review of his finances and came up with this list:

Cash	$13,200
Furniture	1,900
Automobile	21,900
House	210,000
Credit Card	4,600
Student Loan	11,400
Mortgage	100,000

Required

a) Calculate John Bonham's total assets.

b) Calculate John Bonham's total liabilities.

c) Calculate John Bonham's net worth.

AP-3B (❷ ❹)

Consider the following information

Cash	$6,000
Automobile	50,000
Prepaid Insurance	3,000
Bank Loan	10,000
Unpaid Credit Card Bills	2,000
Net Worth	?

How much is the net worth?

AP-4B (❷ ❹ ❺ ❾)

Christine Sutherland compiled the following information on May 31, 2016

Cash	$2,100
Jewellery	3,000
House	186,200
Mortgage	171,800
Net Worth	19,500

Transactions for the month of June 2016

1. Received $4,100 cash for her monthly salary.
2. Paid $590 cash for maintenance on her car.
3. Paid cash for telephone, water and electricity for $540.
4. Purchased an automobile worth $10,600 on credit.
5. Received $30 interest earned on bank deposits.
6. Paid $320 for food with cash.

Required

a) What is the ending balance of cash?

INCREASE +	CASH	DECREASE −

b) What is the surplus or deficit for the accounting period?

c) What is Christine Sutherland's net worth on June 30?

AP-5B (❷ ❸ ❺)

Arthur's financial records show that his assets and net worth as of May 1, 2016 are

Cash	$6,000
Computer	4,000
Contents of Home	17,500
Automobile	20,000
House	137,500
Student Loan	?
Net Worth	113,000

Required

a) Arthur wants to find out how much he owes. Determine his total liabilities.

b) During the month of May, Arthur paid $2,000 for two months of rent in advance ($1,000 per month). Calculate the change in Arthur's cash account and personal net worth.

Transaction	Cash	Net Worth
Effect		

AP-6B (❹)

Calculate the missing amounts in the following table.

	Scenario 1	Scenario 2
Total Assets	$125,900	
Total Liabilities		$33,200
Net Worth	$92,700	$117,100

AP-7B (❶ ❸)

As of December 31, 2015, Deena Balsdon had total assets of $42,800 and total liabilities of $16,700. As of December 31, 2016, Deena's total assets and liabilities increased to $48,900 and $26,100, respectively. Fill out the following table of account balances. How has Deena's net worth changed since 2015?

	As at December 31, 2015	As at December 31, 2016
Net Worth		

____

____

AP-8B (❷ ❹ ❾)

Alan Marshall is preparing his balance sheet and income statement for the month ended July 31, 2016. Use the following information to help him prepare his financial statements.

Opening Balances as at July 1, 2016	
Cash	$4,400
Contents of Home	2,800
Automobile	4,800
House	287,900
Unpaid Accounts	8,500
Mortgage	239,300
Net Worth	52,100

Transactions for the month of July

1. Purchased a $1,600 high definition television using the credit card.
2. Paid a telephone bill of $640 for the month of July using the credit card.
3. Paid credit card bill with cash for $3,300.
4. Purchased $1,010 of groceries and food using cash.
5. Paid July's utilities for $1,100 with cash.
6. Made a principal payment of $1,100 for the mortgage.
7. Deposited $4,700 salary earned during the month.
8. Earned $60 interest on savings account.

Required

a) Using the information provided, record the opening balances in the T-accounts.

b) Record the transactions for the month of July in the T-accounts.

PERSONAL BALANCE SHEET
As at July 31, 2016

ASSETS

Increase	Decrease
+ **CASH**	-
Opening	

Increase	Decrease
+ **CONTENTS OF HOME**	-
Opening	

Increase	Decrease
+ **AUTOMOBILE**	-
Opening	

Increase	Decrease
+ **HOUSE**	-
Opening	

LIABILITIES

Decrease	Increase
- **UNPAID ACCOUNTS**	+
	Opening

Decrease	Increase
- **MORTGAGE**	+
	Opening

NET WORTH

Decrease	Increase
- **NET WORTH**	+
	Opening

Total Assets ______

Total Liabilities ______ } ______

Net Worth ______

PERSONAL INCOME STATEMENT
For the Month Ended July 31, 2016

REVENUE

Decrease	Increase
-	+

LESS EXPENSES

Increase	Decrease
+ **CLOTHING EXPENSE**	-

Increase	Decrease
+ **FOOD EXPENSE**	-

Increase	Decrease
+ **TELEPHONE EXPENSE**	-

Increase	Decrease
+ **UTILITIES EXPENSE**	-

Total Revenue ______

Less Total Expenses ______

Surplus (Deficit) ______

AP-9B (❷❹❺❾)

The following information is available from Tory Barnes' financial records

Opening Balances as at February 1, 2016	
Cash	$34,000
Prepaid Insurance	3,500
Automobile	45,000
Boat	81,000
Unpaid Accounts	21,000
Automobile Loan	25,000
Net Worth	117,500

The following transactions took place during the month of February

1. Purchased fuel for the boat with $85 cash.
2. Earned $1,250 wages and deposited in bank account.
3. Purchased $420 of groceries on a credit card.
4. Won $200 cash from a lottery.
5. Paid $3,600 cash for credit card bills due.
6. Paid $360 interest on credit card bill with cash.
7. Booked a flight on credit for $900.
8. Recognized one month of car insurance used up for $350.

Record the transactions in the T-accounts.

PERSONAL BALANCE SHEET
As at February 29, 2016

ASSETS

Increase | Decrease
+ **CASH** -
Opening

Increase | Decrease
+ **PREPAID INSURANCE** -
Opening

Increase | Decrease
+ **AUTOMOBILE** -
Opening

Increase | Decrease
+ **BOAT** -
Opening

LIABILITIES

Decrease | Increase
- **UNPAID ACCOUNTS** +
Opening

Decrease | Increase
- **AUTOMOBILE LOAN** +
Opening

NET WORTH

Decrease | Increase
- **NET WORTH** +
Opening

Total Assets ______
Total Liabilities ______ } ______
Net Worth ______

INCOME STATEMENT
For the Month Ended February 29, 2016

REVENUE

Decrease | Increase
- | +

LESS EXPENSES

Increase | Decrease
+ **ENTERTAINMENT EXPENSE** -

Increase | Decrease
+ **FOOD EXPENSE** -

Increase | Decrease
+ **FUEL EXPENSE** -

Increase | Decrease
+ **INSURANCE EXPENSE** -

Increase | Decrease
+ **INTEREST EXPENSE** -

Increase | Decrease
+ **TRAVEL EXPENSE** -

Total Revenue ______
Less Total Expenses ______
Surplus (Deficit) ______

Analysis

Tory will be cancelling her auto insurance with no cancellation fee incurred. Which accounts will be affected by the insurance cancellation? How will the balances change?

AP-10B (❷ ❸)

Ethan is a famous songwriter and composer. His income is based solely on royalties that he receives regularly. Ethan opted to use three months as his accounting period.

The following information pertains to income earned and expenses incurred from January 1, 2016 to March 31, 2016

	January	February	March
Royalty Income	$12,000	$13,000	$10,000
Interest Expense	60	60	60
Food Expense	2,000	2,100	1,900
Maintenance Expense	350	500	180
Clothing Expense	900	1,500	0
Utilities Expense	300	500	0
Rent Expense	1,500	1,500	1,500
Miscellaneous Expense	15	50	5

Required

a) Prepare a personal income statement for each of the three months.

Ethan
Personal Income Statement
For the Period Ended March 31, 2016

	January	February	March	Total

b) What amount should be added to Ethan's net worth on March 31, 2016?

AP-11B (❷ ❸)

Archie always prepares an income statement and balance sheet each month, but he has fallen behind. Assume the opening net worth for October 31, 2016 is $6,770. Luckily, he has kept track of his account balances as shown below

	October 31, 2016	November 30, 2016
Cash	$2,500	$6,900
Entertainment Expense	500	250
Food Expense	280	270
Gasoline Expense	140	130
Prepaid Rent	4,200	2,800
Rent Expense	1,400	1,400
Salary	5,050	5,050
Unpaid Accounts	700	700
Automobile	3,500	3,500

Complete the table below.

	October 31, 2016	November 30, 2016
Opening Net Worth		
Surplus (Deficit)		
Closing Net Worth		

Analysis

Archie noticed that his net worth did not increase as much as his cash did during November. Why is this the case?

AP-12B (❷ ❹)

Using the opening balances provided in the balance sheets below, enter the updated amounts for each transaction in the blank balance sheets labelled Answers.

1. Applied for and received a student loan of $5,700.

Opening Balances

Assets		**Liabilities**	
Cash	$5,600	Unpaid Accounts	$2,500
Investment	8,400	Bank Loan	900
Contents of Home	6,200	Automobile Loan	4,800
Automobile	22,300	Student Loan	5,500
House	287,900	Mortgage	241,500
		Total Liabilities	255,200
		Net Worth	75,200
Total Assets	$330,400	**Total Liabilities + Net Worth**	$330,400

Answers

2. Purchased some furniture and jewellery for $5,000 cash.

Opening Balances

Assets		Liabilities	
Cash	$8,200	Unpaid Accounts	$2,400
Investment	7,200	Bank Loan	200
Contents of Home	6,100	Automobile Loan	4,400
Automobile	22,900	Student Loan	6,200
House	272,300	Mortgage	242,200
		Total Liabilities	255,400
		Net Worth	61,300
Total Assets	$316,700	**Total Liabilities + Net Worth**	$316,700

Answers

3. Paid a portion of the principal of the automobile loan for $1,200.

Opening Balances

Assets		Liabilities	
Cash	$4,500	Unpaid Accounts	$2,200
Contents of Home	5,500	Bank Loan	600
Automobile	19,000	Automobile Loan	4,200
House	290,000	Student Loan	6,800
		Mortgage	242,800
		Total Liabilities	256,600
		Net Worth	62,400
Total Assets	$319,000	**Total Liabilities + Net Worth**	$319,000

Answers

4. Bought a motorcycle for $7,100—paid a $1,400 deposit with cash and borrowed $5,700 from the bank.

Opening Balances

Assets		Liabilities	
Cash	$5,000	Unpaid Accounts	$2,000
Contents of Home	6,700	Bank Loan	1,000
Motorcycle	0	Student Loan	11,000
Automobile	17,000	Mortgage	242,000
House	283,300	**Total Liabilities**	256,000
		Net Worth	56,000
Total Assets	$312,000	**Total Liabilities + Net Worth**	$312,000

Answers

AP-13B (8)

Stacey Green received the following amounts in cash for the month of November 2016

Salary	$2,100
Gifts	$240
Winnings at the casino	$170
Performance bonus paid by employer	$460

Calculate Stacey's total revenue and total capital items for November 2016.

AP-14B (4)

Indicate whether the terms of the accounting equation will increase, decrease or stay the same for each transaction by placing a "+" or "–" in the appropriate space. If an item is not changed by the transaction, leave the space blank.The first transaction has been completed for you.

Transaction	Assets	= Liabilities	+ Net Worth
Deposited salary earned.	+		+
1. Purchased a new bicycle on credit.			
2. Purchased groceries on credit.			
3. Borrowed money from the bank.			
4. Purchased a ring for $200 cash.			
5. Received a cash gift.			
6. Made a loan payment with interest.			

AP-15B (❷ ❹ ❾)

The following information is available from Drew Bernard's financial records

Opening Balances as at September 1, 2016	
Cash	$1,500
Automobile	9,400
Boat	18,000
Instruments	7,600
House	415,000
Student Loans	67,000
Unpaid Accounts	8,500
Mortgage	250,000
Net Worth	126,000

The following transactions took place during the month of September

1. Purchased a piano worth $900 using cash.
2. Put $720 food expenses on a credit card.
3. Purchased a $800 guitar on credit.
4. Received cash inheritance of $45,000.
5. Paid off unpaid accounts with $9,570 cash.
6. Received $50 interest on the bank account.

Record the transactions in the T-accounts.

PERSONAL BALANCE SHEET
As at September 30, 2016

ASSETS

Increase	Decrease
+ **CASH**	-
Opening	

Increase	Decrease
+ **AUTOMOBILE**	-
Opening	

Increase	Decrease
+ **BOAT**	-
Opening	

Increase	Decrease
+ **INSTRUMENTS**	-
Opening	

Increase	Decrease
+ **HOUSE**	-
Opening	

LIABILITIES

Decrease	Increase
- **STUDENT LOANS**	+
	Opening

Decrease	Increase
- **UNPAID ACCOUNTS**	+
	Opening

Decrease	Increase
- **MORTGAGE**	+
	Opening

Decrease	Increase
- **NET WORTH**	+
	Opening

Total Assets ______

Total Liabilities ______

Net Worth ______

} ______

INCOME STATEMENT
For the Month Ended September 30, 2016

REVENUE

Decrease	Increase
-	+

LESS EXPENSES

Increase	Decrease
+ **ENTERTAINMENT EXPENSE**	-

Increase	Decrease
+ **GROCERIES EXPENSE**	-

Increase	Decrease
+ **INTEREST EXPENSE**	-

Increase	Decrease
+ **MAINTENANCE EXPENSE**	-

Total Revenue ______

Less Total Expenses ______

Surplus (Deficit) ______

AP-16B (❹ ❾)

Indicate whether assets, liabilities or net worth will increase or decrease and by how much, based on each transaction. The first one has been done for you. Always ensure the accounting equation is balanced.

Provide an explanation only if net worth is affected.

	Assets	= Liabilities	+ Net Worth	Explanation
1. Purchased a new television for $700 on credit.	+700	+700		
2. Won $700 in a lottery.				
3. Deposited a $2,800 salary earned.				
4. Purchased furniture for $400 in cash.				
5. Transferred $500 of a chequing account to savings.				
6. Paid $150 for concert tickets with a credit card.				
7. Paid $200 cash for utilities.				
8. Paid $1,500 toward the mortgage.				
9. Paid $1,100 toward unpaid bills.				

AP-17B (❹ ❾)

The following information is available from Lily's financial record

Opening Balances as at November 1, 2016	
Cash	$18,000
Furniture	3,100
Valuables & Electronics	3,200
House	255,000
Student Loans	39,000
Mortgage	100,000
Family Loan	2,000
Net Worth	138,300

Indicate whether the account balances will increase or decrease and by how much, based on each transaction. Always ensure the accounting equation is balanced.

	Assets	= Liabilities	+ Net Worth	Explanation
1. Purchased $1,600 of new furniture for the bedroom with cash.				
2. Won a tablet worth $800 as a raffle prize.				
3. $350 was taken from the bank account for a car lease payment.				
4. Family member accepted $2,000 worth of jewellery in repayment of the loan.				
5. Made a $2,000 mortgage payment with cash. Includes $400 of interest.				
6. Paid $1,000 towards the student loans with cash. Includes $140 of interest.				
7. Salary earned of $4,800 was directly deposited to the bank account.				

Analysis

The net worth account is only updated at the end of an accounting period. Revenue and expense accounts, and the net worth account track changes in net worth during the period. For each transaction that affects net worth, determine whether a revenue, expense, or net worth is used to track the change.

____

____

____

____

____

AP-18B (❷)

Consider the following financial information of Pete Griphin

Automobile	$66,000
Boat	55,000
Automobile Loan	50,000
Cash	14,500
Coin Collection	1,200
Cottage	84,000
House and Property	510,000
Prepaid House Insurance	8,500
Mortgage Principal	450,000
Trailer	4,000

Required

a) Calculate Pete's total assets.

b) Calculate Pete's total liabilities.

c) Calculate Pete's net worth.

Analysis

Pete makes payments against his liabilities and updates all of his account balances at the end of each month. Which account balances will change at the end of the month? Which will increase and which will decrease?

AP-19B (❹ ❺ ❻)

Jess Day stored her personal accounting information in the computer but some of it was deleted by accident.

Appliances	$1,100
Cell Phone	500
Family Loan	?
Jewellery	800
Net Worth	4,500
Unpaid Bills	350
Automobile	5,000

Required

a) What are Jess' total assets?

____

____

b) What is the amount of Jess' family loan?

____

____

____

____

Analysis

Jess works as a teacher. She has agreed to work as a substitute during one day next week for extra wages. According to accrual-based accounting, has Jess' net worth increased? Why or why not?

____

____

____

AP-20B (❹ ❺ ❼)

Dex had the following transactions during the month of May

1. Purchased a new laptop for $1,200 cash.
2. Put $1,600 of car repairs on his credit card.
3. Spent $80 on a steak dinner with his sister and paid with his credit card.
4. Prepaid his son's nanny $850 cash for future services.
5. Received salary of $5,500.

How have these transactions affected Dex's net worth?

Analysis

Has Dex's cash changed the same amount as his net worth? Why or why not?

AP-21B (❷ ❺ ❾)

On June 1, 2016, Joey had $3,100 in cash (including his bank account). The following transactions took place for the month of June

1. Returned a newly purchased cell phone to the store for $150 cash.
2. Purchased a new laptop for $1,200 cash.
3. Went to a concert—ticket price was $90 paid by cash.
4. Received wages of $3,200 for the month.
5. Spent $300 cash on food for the month.
6. Received monthly utility bills of $310, due July 21.
7. Received interest on a savings account of $35.

Required

a) What is the balance of cash on June 30?

INCREASE +	CASH	DECREASE –

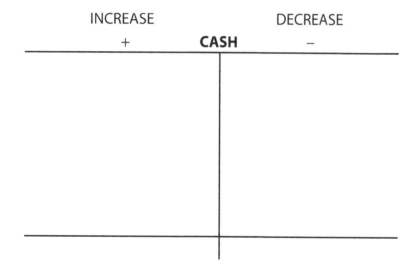

b) Prepare a personal income statement for Joey for June.

Personal Income Statement		
For the Month Ended June 30, 2016		
Revenue		
Expenses		
Surplus (Deficit)		

Analysis

Joey purchased his car using 0% financing. This means there is no interest on the loan. What is the effect on net worth after each car payment? Would the effect be any different if the loan had interest? Explain.

AP-22B (❹)

Rita has total assets of $35,000 and total liabilities of $20,000. She owns a few pieces of gold jewellery that were originally purchased for $1,000 total. She recently purchased some additional jewellery for $3,000 cash. Which account balances will change from this transaction and by how much? Use the accounting equation to check your answer.

Analysis

Rita wants to increase her net worth so she decided to purchase a new automobile by getting a bank loan. Has her net worth changed as expected? Explain.

AP-23B (❷ ❹ ❺)

Jed Mosley had the following financial data for the year ended December 31, 2016

Automobile	$6,500
Chequing Account	1,100
Credit Card Bill	2,100
Electronics	1,000
Furniture	2,000
Hydro Bill	120
Phone Bill	150
Savings Account	10,000

Required

a) Calculate Jed's total assets.

b) Calculate Jed's total liabilities.

Analysis

Jed realized he has a rent payment coming up on January 1, 2017 that will cover January's rent. Should this be included in December's financial data? Explain.

Case Study

CS-1 (2 4 5 6 7 8 9)

After taking the first part of this financial accounting course, you excitedly tell a friend what you have learned. You tell him about assets, liabilities and net worth and how they increase and decrease in value with every financial transaction. Your friend decides to start getting organized and apply accounting principles to his personal finances. He compiles everything that he thinks is important and calculates his net worth. He then asks you to look over what he had done to make sure it is correct. His list of important financial items is listed below, along with his version of the T-account records.

1. He had $950 in his bank account at the beginning of the month.
2. He had a $1,200 balance on his credit card at the beginning of the month.
3. He estimates that he had about $3,000 worth of "stuff" in his apartment at the beginning of the month (TV, sound system, computer and furniture).
4. Deposited his salary of $1,500.
5. Paid in advance for three months of rent with $1,350 cash.
6. Paid $600 to pay off a portion of the credit card bill.
7. Purchased a new video game system for $350 with his credit card.
8. Bought $120 worth of food with cash.
9. Got hired at a second job. He will start next month and will earn $800 per month.
10. Spent $250 cash on movies, stage plays and Dave and Buster's.
11. Lived in his apartment for one of the three months he already paid for (see #5)

+	CASH		-
1.	$950	5.	$1,350
4.	1,500	6.	600
		8.	120
		10.	250
Total	$130		

-	UNPAID ACCOUNTS		+
6.	$600	2.	$1,200
		7.	350
		Total	$950

-	NET WORTH		+
5.	$1,350	3.	$3,000
8.	120	4.	1,500
10.	250	7.	350
		9.	800
		Total	$3,930

Required

a) What are some immediate problems that you see with what your friend has prepared?

____

____

____

____

b) With all the problems you see, your friend asks you to show him what the correct records should look like. Use the templates at the end of this problem to record the transactions.

____

After showing your friend the corrected version, he asks a number of questions.

c) Why did you use all of these accounts when I only used three (Cash, Unpaid Accounts and Net Worth)?

____

____

____

____

____

d) Why is the $3,000 worth of "stuff" not considered net worth?

____

____

____

____

____

____

e) I was having trouble figuring out how to record my second job which I start next month. They are going to be paying me $800 a month! I figured it will increase my net worth, but I didn't know where else to put it. I knew it couldn't be cash, because they haven't paid me yet. What did you do with it and why?

f) What did you do with my rent? Shouldn't the entire $1,350 decrease my net worth? And what would happen if I did it my way?

g) I forgot to tell you that the $600 credit card payment included $30 of interest. I didn't think it mattered since the total payment amount is the same. This won't change anything, right?

h) You may have noticed that I am running low on cash. Any suggestions on how I can raise more cash?

i) This is very useful and I would like to do this more often. I can do it this weekend, then two weeks from now once I finish my exams, then probably not for another month after that. I'm going on a well-deserved vacation after my exams, so I won't be around to look after it. Do you think this will work out well?

PERSONAL BALANCE SHEET

Assets		Liabilities	
INCREASE +	DECREASE -	DECREASE -	INCREASE +
Opening:			Opening:

INCREASE +	DECREASE -	DECREASE -	INCREASE +
Opening:			Opening:

INCREASE +	DECREASE -	DECREASE -	INCREASE +
Opening:			Opening:

Total Assets	
Total Liabilities	
Net Worth	

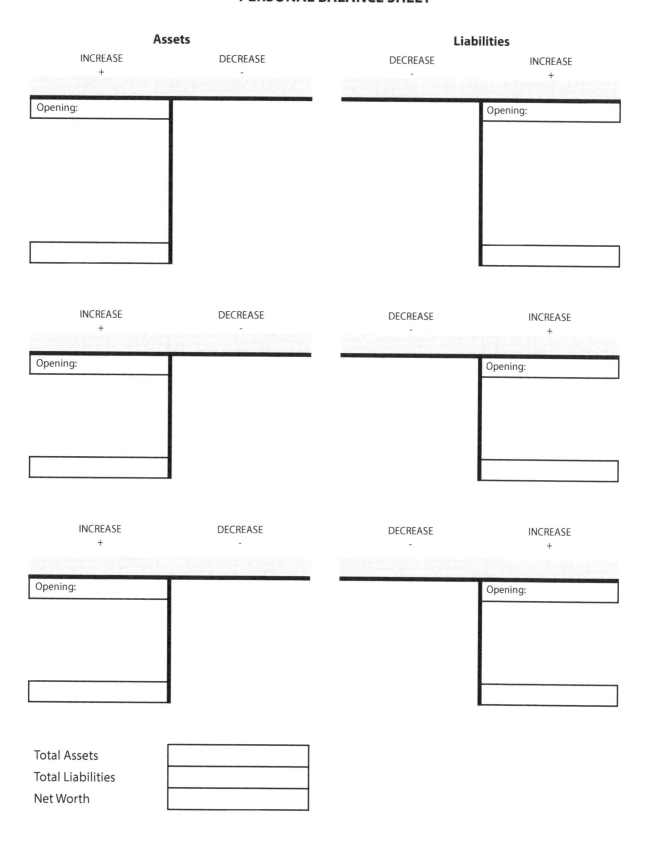

PERSONAL INCOME STATEMENT

DECREASE - | **REVENUE** | INCREASE +

LESS EXPENSES

INCREASE + | DECREASE -

INCREASE + | DECREASE -

INCREASE + | DECREASE -

INCREASE + | DECREASE -

INCREASE + | DECREASE -

INCREASE + | DECREASE -

Total Revenue	
Less Total Expenses	
Surplus (Deficit)	

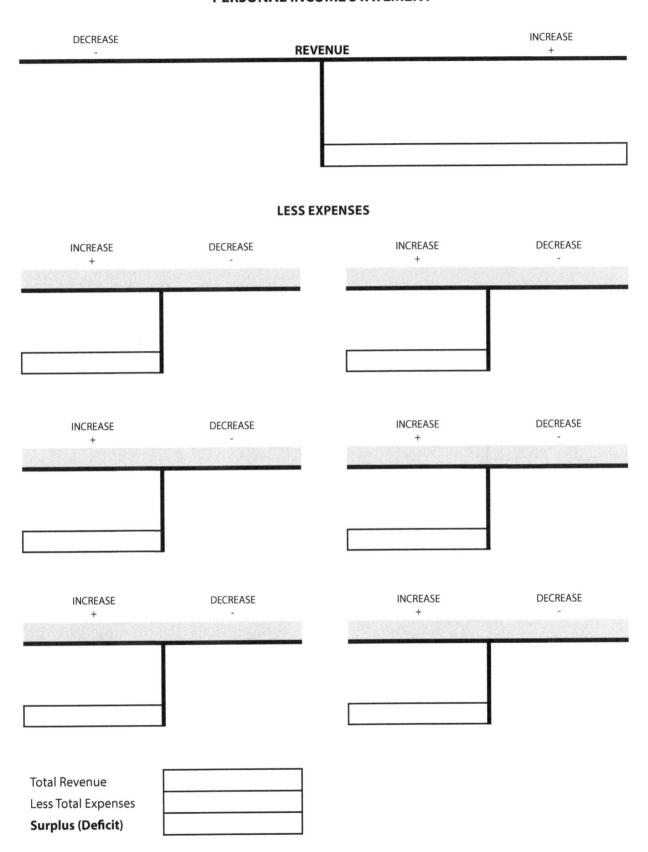

Chapter 2

LINKING PERSONAL ACCOUNTING TO BUSINESS ACCOUNTING

LEARNING OUTCOMES

1. List the differences between personal accounts and business accounts
2. Describe the sequence of assets and liabilities as they appear on the balance sheet
3. Define equity and calculate the balance of the capital account
4. Describe the three main types of businesses
5. Record revenue based on the concept of accruals
6. Record expenses based on the concept of accruals
7. Record business transactions in T-accounts

AMEENGAGE™ *Access **ameengage.com** for integrated resources including tutorials, practice exercises, the digital textbook and more.*

Assessment Questions

AS-1 (1)

Net worth in personal accounting is similar to which item in accounting for businesses?

AS-2 (2)

In what order are the assets of a business listed? Explain.

AS-3 (2)

In what order are the liabilities of a business listed? Explain.

AS-4 (❸)

What is equity?

____

____

____

AS-5 (❸)

What is the formula for calculating the ending owner's equity balance?

____

____

AS-6 (❸)

Describe owner's contributions and owner's drawings and explain how they affect the balance sheet.

____

____

____

AS-7 (❹)

List the three main types of businesses.

____

____

AS-8 (❹)

Describe what a service business does. Provide two examples of service businesses.

____

____

____

AS-9 (❹)

Describe what a merchandising business does. Provide an example of a merchandising business.

AS-10 (❹)

Describe what a manufacturing business does. Provide two examples of a manufacturing business.

AS-11 (❻)

Give three examples of expenses that businesses commonly prepay.

AS-12 (❻)

Describe the three different times cash can be paid to a supplier related to an expense.

AS-13 (6)

What does it mean to *incur* an expense?

AS-14 (6)

What is the entry to record an expense if a company pays *when* the expense is incurred?

AS-15 (6)

What is the entry to record an expense if a company pays *after* the expense is incurred?

AS-16 (6)

What is the entry if a company pays *before* the expense is incurred?

AS-17 (5)

What does it mean to *recognize* revenue?

AS-18 (❺)

Describe the three different times cash can be received from a customer related to earning revenue.

AS-19 (❺)

What is the entry to record revenue if a customer pays *when* the service is delivered?

AS-20 (❺)

What is the entry to record revenue if a customer pays *after* the service is delivered?

AS-21 (❺)

What is the entry if a customer pays *before* the service is delivered?

AS-22 (❺)

What type of account is unearned revenue?

Application Questions Group A

AP-1A (❸ ❺ ❻)

For each transaction, indicate whether the total assets (A), liabilities (L) or owner's equity (OE) increased (+), decreased (–) or did not change (o) by placing the symbol in the appropriate column.

		A	L	OE
1.	Paid salaries for current month.			
2.	Purchased equipment on credit.			
3.	Purchased furniture using cash.			
4.	Additional investment into the business.			
5.	Received payment for services to be provided next month.			
6.	Made partial payment for equipment purchased on credit.			
7.	Billed customers for services performed.			
8.	Withdrew cash for personal use.			
9.	Received payment from customers already billed.			
10.	Received bills for utilities to be paid next month.			

AP-2A (❸ ❺ ❻)

The given transactions were completed by Juliet's Delivery Services during May 2016. Indicate the effects of each transaction by placing the appropriate letter in the space provided.

A Increase in asset, decrease in another asset
B Increase in asset, increase in liability
C Increase in asset, increase in owner's equity
D Decrease in asset, decrease in liability
E Decrease in asset, decrease in owner's equity

____ Received cash for providing delivery services.
____ Paid amount owing that was outstanding to a creditor.
____ Invested additional cash in the business.
____ Paid advertising expense with cash.
____ Billed customers for delivery services on account.
____ Purchased office furniture on account.
____ Paid rent for the month.
____ Received cash from customers on account.
____ Received cash in advance for services to be provided in the next month.
____ Owner withdrew cash for personal use.

AP-3A (❷)

Organize the following asset and liability accounts in the order they are likely to appear in a balance sheet.

Assets	Liabilities
Accounts Receivable	Bank Loan
Cash	Accounts Payable
Equipment	Unearned Revenue
Prepaid Expenses	

AP-4A (❺ ❻)

Simpson Moving had the following transactions during the month. Indicate whether assets, liabilities or owner's equity will increase or decrease and by how much, based on each transaction. Provide an explanation only if equity is affected. The first entry has been done for you. Always ensure the accounting equation is balanced.

	Assets	= Liabilities	+ Owner's Equity	Explanation
1. Paid $200 cash for maintenance expense.	-200		-200	Paid for maintenance expense
2. The owner invested $4,000 cash in the business.				
3. Paid $2,400 cash for one year insurance.				
4. Received a telephone bill for $150, which will be paid later.				
5. Purchased equipment worth $1,000 on account.				
6. Provided services and collected $4,200 cash.				
7. Paid $500 towards the bank loan.				
8. Paid $50 interest related to the bank loan.				
9. Paid $700 of accounts payable.				

AP-5A (❺ ❻ ❼)

Dry Cleanest offers extensive dry cleaning services. Amy York started this company one year ago. The opening balances of the accounts on August 1, 2016 are shown below.

Cash	$980
Accounts Receivable	620
Prepaid Expenses	300
Machinery	3,800
Accounts Payable	1,020
Bank Loan	0
York, Capital	4,680

Required

a) Indicate whether assets, liabilities or owner's equity will increase or decrease and by how much, based on each transaction during August. Provide an explanation only if equity is affected. The first one has been done for you. Always ensure the accounting equation is balanced.

b) Record the transactions in the T-accounts.

	Assets	= Liabilities	+ Owner's Equity	Explanation
1. Borrowed $10,000 from the bank.	+10,000	+10,000		
2. Purchased machinery for $7,300 cash.				
3. Billed clients $2,950 for completed services. Due in 30 days.				
4. Paid $130 cash for regular maintenance on the machine.				
5. Collected $1,300 from clients who owed money.				
6. Paid 4 months' rent of $3,000 in advance.				
7. Recorded $1,600 of cash sales for the month.				
8. Paid $700 owed to a supplier.				

Dry Cleanest
Balance Sheet
As at August 31, 2016

ASSETS

INCREASE		DECREASE
+	CASH	-
Opening		

INCREASE		DECREASE
+	ACCOUNTS RECEIVABLE	-
Opening		

INCREASE		DECREASE
+	PREPAID EXPENSES	-
Opening		

INCREASE		DECREASE
+	MACHINERY	-
Opening		

LIABILITIES

DECREASE		INCREASE
-	ACCOUNTS PAYABLE	+
		Opening

DECREASE		INCREASE
-	BANK LOAN	+
		Opening

OWNER'S EQUITY

DECREASE		INCREASE
-	YORK, CAPITAL	+
		Opening

INCREASE		DECREASE
+	YORK, DRAWINGS	-

TOTAL ASSETS ______

TOTAL LIABILITIES ______ } ______

OWNER'S EQUITY ______

Dry Cleanest
Income Statement
For the Month Ended August 31, 2016

REVENUE

DECREASE		INCREASE
-	SERVICE REVENUE	+

LESS EXPENSES

INCREASE		DECREASE
+	INSURANCE EXPENSE	-

INCREASE		DECREASE
+	MAINTENANCE EXPENSE	-

INCREASE		DECREASE
+	SALARIES EXPENSE	-

INCREASE		DECREASE
+	UTILITIES EXPENSE	-

TOTAL REVENUE ______

LESS TOTAL EXPENSES ______

NET INCOME (LOSS) ______

Analysis

The owner of Dry Cleanest wants to withdraw cash from the business, but she does not want the net income to fall below $4,000. What is the maximum amount of cash she can withdraw in order to keep net income from falling below $4,000? Explain.

____

____

____

____

____

AP-6A (❷❸)

Alex Limbo is the owner of Double Duplicator. The following is a list of Double Duplicator's accounts and balances as at March 31, 2016.

Cash	$4,700
Limbo, Capital	2,000
Accounts Payable	5,000
Unearned Revenue	2,000
Prepaid Insurance	2,300
Bank Loan	10,000
Automobile Loan	18,000
Prepaid Rent	5,000
Automobile	25,000

Required

Prepare a balance sheet using the above information.

Double Duplicators
Balance Sheet
As at March 31, 2016

AP-7A (❸ ❺ ❻ ❼)

Jessica Holmes recently started her own shoe repair business. Transactions for the first month of operations (June 2016) are as follows.

1. Jessica invested $10,000 cash in the business.
2. Paid two months of rent for $1,000 in advance.
3. Purchased store equipment worth $3,000 with cash.
4. Incurred business registration expenses, paid with $600 cash.
5. Paid travel expenses with $1,100 cash.
6. Received $2,300 cash from customers for shoe repair services performed during the month.
7. Provided shoe repair services worth $1,200 on account.
8. Paid $1,300 salary to an assistant.
9. Borrowed $3,000 cash from the bank.
10. Received $800 in bills for electricity, water and telephone, to be paid next month.
11. Jessica withdrew $500 cash for personal purposes.
12. Received $200 owing from a customer for service provided earlier this month.

Required

Record the above transactions on the T-account worksheet.

Holmes Shoe Repair
Balance Sheet
As at June 30, 2016

ASSETS

INCREASE	DECREASE
+ **CASH**	-

INCREASE	DECREASE
+ **ACCOUNTS RECEIVABLE**	-

INCREASE	DECREASE
+ **PREPAID RENT**	-

INCREASE	DECREASE
+ **EQUIPMENT**	-

LIABILITIES

DECREASE	INCREASE
- **ACCOUNTS PAYABLE**	+

DECREASE	INCREASE
- **BANK LOAN**	+

OWNER'S EQUITY

DECREASE	INCREASE
- **HOLMES, CAPITAL**	+

INCREASE	DECREASE
+ **HOLMES, DRAWINGS**	-

TOTAL ASSETS ________

TOTAL LIABILITIES ________

OWNER'S EQUITY ________ } ________

Holmes Shoe Repair
Income Statement
For the Month Ended June 30, 2016

REVENUE

DECREASE	INCREASE
- **SERVICE REVENUE**	+

LESS EXPENSES

INCREASE	DECREASE
+ **REGISTRATION AND LICENSES EXPENSE**	-

INCREASE	DECREASE
+ **RENT EXPENSE**	-

INCREASE	DECREASE
+ **SALARIES EXPENSE**	-

INCREASE	DECREASE
+ **TELEPHONE & UTILITIES EXPENSE**	-

INCREASE	DECREASE
+ **TRAVEL EXPENSE**	-

TOTAL REVENUE ________

LESS TOTAL EXPENSES ________

NET INCOME (LOSS) ________

AP-8A (❸ ❺ ❻ ❼)

Sheila Abney opened a dormitory locator business called Dormitory Locators near a college campus. During the first month of operations, June 2016, Sheila had the following transactions.

1. Invested $10,000 of personal funds to start the business.
2. Incurred travel expenses for $650, which will be paid later.
3. Paid $700 cash for maintenance expense.
4. Received $5,000 cash for services provided to clients.
5. Paid $650 for the on account purchase in transaction 2.
6. Paid three months of office rent costing $1,500 in advance.
7. Incurred $300 of utilities expense, which will be paid next month.
8. Received $1,000 cash from a customer for services to be provided in two months.
9. Provided $1,200 in services for a customer who will pay later.
10. Recognized one month of office rent that was previously prepaid.
11. Sheila withdrew $1,000 cash for personal use.
12. Purchased second-hand car worth $10,000 for business use with cash.
13. Received $700 from the customer owing for the service provided earlier this month.

Required

Prepare a T-account worksheet.

Dormitory Locators
Balance Sheet
As at June 30, 2016

ASSETS

INCREASE +	DECREASE -
Opening	

INCREASE +	DECREASE -
Opening	

INCREASE +	DECREASE -
Opening	

INCREASE +	DECREASE -
Opening	

LIABILITIES

DECREASE -	INCREASE +
	Opening

DECREASE -	INCREASE +
	Opening

DECREASE -	INCREASE +
	Opening

OWNER'S EQUITY

DECREASE -	INCREASE +
	Opening

INCREASE +	DECREASE -

TOTAL ASSETS ______

TOTAL LIABILITIES ______

OWNER'S EQUITY ______ } ______

Dormitory Locators
Income Statement
For the Month Ended June 30, 2016

REVENUE

DECREASE -	INCREASE +

LESS EXPENSES

INCREASE +	DECREASE -

INCREASE +	DECREASE -

INCREASE +	DECREASE -

INCREASE +	DECREASE -

INCREASE +	DECREASE -

TOTAL REVENUE ______

LESS TOTAL EXPENSES ______

NET INCOME (LOSS) ______

AP-9A (❸ ❺ ❻ ❼)

Jeff Roberts Communications is a public relations firm. On April 30, 2016, the firm had the following ending balances:

Cash	$20,000
Prepaid Rent	10,000
Equipment	25,000
Accounts Payable	8,000
Roberts, Capital	47,000

During the month of May, the company completed the following transactions

1. Purchased $800 of office equipment on account.
2. Paid $6,000 to reduce amount owing to a supplier.
3. Received $5,000 cash from customers for services rendered.
4. Paid utilities bill for May with $700 cash.
5. Purchased a computer worth $1,500 on account.
6. Received a bill for $1,000 to be paid in July for advertisements placed in a national newspaper during the month of May to promote Jeff Roberts Communications.
7. Paid May's salaries with $1,900 cash.
8. Withdrew $3,000 cash for personal use.
9. Recognized $2,000 rent for May (which was previously prepaid).
10. Received $4,000 cash in advance for a contract to be completed in three months.

Required

Prepare the T-account worksheet.

Note: the ending balance for the month of April is the opening balance for the month of May.

Roberts Communications
Balance Sheet
As at May 31, 2016

ASSETS

INCREASE + DECREASE -
Opening

INCREASE + DECREASE -
Opening

INCREASE + DECREASE -
Opening

LIABILITIES

DECREASE - INCREASE +
Opening

DECREASE - INCREASE +
Opening

DECREASE - INCREASE +
Opening

OWNER'S EQUITY

DECREASE - INCREASE +
Opening

INCREASE + DECREASE -

TOTAL ASSETS ______

TOTAL LIABILITIES ______

OWNER'S EQUITY ______ } ______

Roberts Communications
Income Statement
For the Month Ended May 31, 2016

REVENUE

DECREASE - INCREASE +

LESS EXPENSES

INCREASE + DECREASE -

INCREASE + DECREASE -

INCREASE + DECREASE -

INCREASE + DECREASE -

INCREASE DECREASE

TOTAL REVENUE ______

LESS TOTAL EXPENSES ______

NET INCOME (LOSS) ______

AP-10A (❸❺❻❼)

On December 1, 2016, Sheila Ann established City Laundry. During the first month, the following transactions occurred

1. Sheila Ann deposited $15,000 into City Laundry's bank account.
2. Bought tables and chairs worth $1,000 with cash.
3. Received and paid utilities bill for $1,200 in cash.
4. Purchased washers and dryers worth $4,000; paying $2,000 cash with the remainder due in 30 days.
5. Purchased two additional dryers worth $1,100 from Marky Distributors, on account.
6. Received $4,000 cash for laundry services provided for the first half of the month.
7. Paid $900 cash for a one-year insurance policy.
8. Paid $1,000 cash for current month's rent.
9. Paid the amount owing to Marky Distributors.
10. Provided $3,500 of laundry services during the second half of the month for customers who will pay at a later date.
11. Paid employee salaries of $1,400.
12. Sheila withdrew $2,000 cash for personal use.
13. Recorded first month's insurance expense of $75.
14. Collected $3,000 cash from customers as payment on their account.
15. Received $2,000 cash in advance for services to be provided next year.

Required

Prepare the T-account worksheet.

City Laundry
Balance Sheet
As at December 31, 2016

ASSETS

INCREASE DECREASE
\+ -
Opening

INCREASE DECREASE
\+ -
Opening

INCREASE DECREASE
\+ -
Opening

INCREASE DECREASE
\+ -
Opening

LIABILITIES

DECREASE INCREASE
\- +
Opening

DECREASE INCREASE
\- +
Opening

OWNER'S EQUITY

DECREASE INCREASE
\- +
Opening

INCREASE DECREASE
\+ -

TOTAL ASSETS ______

TOTAL LIABILITIES ______ } ______

OWNER'S EQUITY ______

City Laundry
Income Statement
For the Month Ended December 31, 2016

REVENUE

DECREASE INCREASE
\- +

LESS EXPENSES

INCREASE DECREASE
\+ -

INCREASE DECREASE
\+ -

INCREASE DECREASE
\+ -

INCREASE DECREASE
\+ -

INCREASE DECREASE

INCREASE DECREASE

TOTAL REVENUE ______

LESS TOTAL EXPENSES ______

NET INCOME (LOSS) ______

AP-11A (❸ ❺ ❻ ❼)

On April 1, 2016, Aaron Ragan established a business to manage rental properties. He had the following transactions during its first month of operations.

1. Owner invested $20,000 cash into the business from his personal savings. This amount was deposited into the business Cash account.
2. Purchased $1,000 office equipment on account.
3. Received $5,000 cash for managing rental properties for a client.
4. Purchased furniture worth $350 on account.
5. Paid utilities bill of $400 for the month in cash.
6. Used a bank loan to purchase office furniture for $5,000.
7. Paid $500 cash to reduce the amount of bank loan principal.
8. Paid rent for the month with $1,800 cash.
9. Paid office staff salaries with $1,500 cash.
10. Withdrew $1,000 cash for personal use.
11. Provided $2,000 of services for a customer on account.

Required

Prepare the T-account worksheet.

Ragan Properties
Balance Sheet
As at April 30, 2016

ASSETS

INCREASE + | DECREASE -
Opening

INCREASE + | DECREASE -
Opening

INCREASE + | DECREASE -
Opening

LIABILITIES

DECREASE - | INCREASE +
Opening

DECREASE - | INCREASE +
Opening

OWNER'S EQUITY

DECREASE - | INCREASE +
Opening

INCREASE + | DECREASE -

TOTAL ASSETS ______

TOTAL LIABILITIES ______

OWNER'S EQUITY ______ } ______

Ragan Properties
Income Statement
For the Month Ended April 30, 2016

REVENUE

DECREASE - | INCREASE +

LESS EXPENSES

INCREASE + | DECREASE -

INCREASE + | DECREASE -

INCREASE + | DECREASE -

INCREASE | DECREASE

INCREASE | DECREASE

TOTAL REVENUE ______

LESS TOTAL EXPENSES ______

NET INCOME (LOSS) ______

AP-12A (❸ ❺ ❻ ❼)

Edward James decided to start his own rent-a-car business after graduation, and recorded these transactions during the first month of operations (January 2016)

1. Edward invested $20,000 cash in the business.
2. Borrowed $20,000 from the bank.
3. Paid $35,000 cash for a new car to be used in the business.
4. Paid the principal of the bank loan with $2,000 cash.
5. Paid for $800 of maintenance expense with cash.
6. Paid monthly salaries for personnel with $1,000 cash.
7. Paid miscellaneous expenses with $300 cash.
8. Received $8,000 service revenue in cash for the month.
9. Received $600 of utilities bill for the month, payable next month.
10. Paid monthly interest on the bank loan with $200 cash.
11. Paid $1,500 of insurance for the next five months in advance.
12. Edward withdrew $1,000 cash for personal use.
13. Received $3,000 cash from customers for services to be provided next month.

Required

Prepare the T-account worksheet, income statement, statement of owner's equity, and balance sheet.

James' Rent-A-Car
Balance Sheet
As at January 31, 2016

ASSETS

INCREASE DECREASE
\+ **CASH** -

INCREASE DECREASE
\+ **PREPAID INSURANCE** -

INCREASE DECREASE
\+ **AUTOMOBILE** -

LIABILITIES

DECREASE INCREASE
\- **ACCOUNTS PAYABLE** +

DECREASE INCREASE
\- **UNEARNED REVENUE** +

DECREASE INCREASE
\- **BANK LOAN** +

OWNER'S EQUITY

DECREASE INCREASE
\- **JAMES, CAPITAL** +

INCREASE DECREASE
\+ **JAMES, DRAWINGS** -

TOTAL ASSETS ________

TOTAL LIABILITIES ________

OWNER'S EQUITY ________ } ________

James' Rent-A-Car
Income Statement
For the Month Ended January 31, 2016

REVENUE

DECREASE INCREASE
\- **SERVICE REVENUE** +

LESS EXPENSES

INCREASE DECREASE
\+ **INTEREST EXPENSE** -

INCREASE DECREASE
\+ **MAINTENANCE EXPENSE** -

INCREASE DECREASE
\+ **MISCELLANEOUS EXPENSE** -

INCREASE DECREASE
\+ **RENT EXPENSE** -

INCREASE DECREASE
\+ **SALARIES EXPENSE** -

INCREASE DECREASE
\+ **UTILITIES EXPENSE** -

TOTAL REVENUE ________

LESS TOTAL EXPENSES ________

NET INCOME (LOSS) ________

James' Rent-A-Car
Income Statement
For the Month Ended January 31, 2016

James' Rent-A-Car
Statement of Owner's Equity
For the Month Ended January 31, 2016

James' Rent-A-Car
Balance Sheet
As at January 31, 2016

AP-13A (❸❺❻❼)

Jessica Cooper is the owner of Jessica's Computer Services. The balance sheet of Jessica's Computer Services on February 29, 2016 is shown below.

Jessica's Computer Services Balance Sheet As at February 29, 2016			
Assets		**Liabilities**	
Cash	$4,000	Accounts Payable	$3,000
Prepaid Insurance	3,000	Bank Loan	0
Furniture and Equipment	25,000		
		Total Liabilities	3,000
		Owner's Equity	
		Cooper, Capital	29,000
Total Assets	$32,000	**Total Liabilities and Owner's Equity**	$32,000

During March, the business engaged in the following transactions

1. Borrowed $20,000 from bank.
2. Purchased computer equipment for $5,000 cash.
3. Performed services for a customer and received $4,000 cash.
4. Purchased furniture for $1,000 on credit.
5. Paid $1,500 to a supplier for the amount owed.
6. Paid the following expenses in cash: salaries $1,000; rent, $1,500; and interest, $200.
7. Received a $900 utilities bill, due next month.
8. Withdrew $3,500 cash for personal use.
9. Received $1,000 cash in advance for services to be completed next month.

Required

Prepare the T-account worksheet, income statement, statement of owner's equity, and balance sheet.

Note: the ending balance for the month of February is the opening balance for the month of March.

Jessica's Computer Services
Balance Sheet
As at March 31, 2016

ASSETS

INCREASE DECREASE
\+ -
Opening

INCREASE DECREASE
\+ -
Opening

INCREASE DECREASE
\+ -
Opening

LIABILITIES

DECREASE INCREASE
\- +
Opening

DECREASE INCREASE
\- +
Opening

DECREASE INCREASE
\- +
Opening

OWNER'S EQUITY

DECREASE INCREASE
\- +
Opening

INCREASE DECREASE
\+ -

TOTAL ASSETS ______
TOTAL LIABILITIES ______
OWNER'S EQUITY ______

Jessica's Computer Services
Income Statement
For the Month Ended March 31, 2016

REVENUE

DECREASE INCREASE
\- +

LESS EXPENSES

INCREASE DECREASE
\+ -

INCREASE DECREASE
\+ -

INCREASE DECREASE
\+ -

INCREASE DECREASE
\+ -

INCREASE DECREASE
\+ -

INCREASE DECREASE
\+ -

TOTAL REVENUE ______
LESS TOTAL EXPENSES ______
NET INCOME (LOSS) ______

Jessica's Computer Services Income Statement For the Month Ended March 31, 2016		

Jessica's Computer Services Statement of Owner's Equity For the Month Ended March 31, 2016		

Jessica's Computer Services Balance Sheet As at March 31, 2016			

Application Questions Group B

AP-1B (❸ ❺ ❻)

For each of the given transactions, determine the effect on owner's equity by placing a checkmark in the space provided.

		Effect on Owner's Equity		
		Increase	Decrease	No Effect
1.	Invested money in the business.			
2.	Purchased equipment on account.			
3.	Paid one third of the amount owing for the purchase of equipment.			
4.	Received cash for the services rendered.			
5.	Paid salaries for the month.			
6.	Withdrew cash for personal use.			
7.	Paid monthly rent.			
8.	Additional investment by the owner.			
9.	Provided services for a customer who will pay in two months.			
10.	Acquired land using cash.			

AP-2B (❸ ❺ ❻)

For the following transactions, fill in the table on the right with the two accounts related to each transaction.

		Account 1	Account 2
1.	Invested cash in the business.		
2.	Purchased service vehicle for business use.		
3.	Collected cash for services provided today.		
4.	Provided services this week on credit.		
5.	Paid operating expenses in cash.		
6.	Received a bill for operating expenses incurred this week.		
7.	Received a loan from the bank.		
8.	Collected cash from a customer for services provided previously.		
9.	Paid monthly salaries to employees with cash.		
10.	Incurred operating expenses this week, to be paid next month.		
11.	Paid cash for expenses incurred previously.		
12.	Received cash in advance for the service to be performed next month.		

AP-3B (❶ ❹)

Match each term with the appropriate description.

A Merchandising
B Service
C Manufacturing
D Accounts Receivable
E Cash

____ A law firm is an example of this type of business.
____ This account represents the amount owed to the business by its customers for services performed earlier.
____ This type of business buys goods to resell to customers.
____ An automaker is an example of this type of business.
____ This is the most liquid asset.

AP-4B (❺ ❻)

Focus In had the following transactions during the month. Indicate whether assets, liabilities or owner's equity will increase or decrease and by how much, based on each transaction. Provide an explanation only if equity is affected. Always ensure the accounting equation is balanced.

	Assets =	Liabilities+	Owner's Equity	Explanation
1. The owner invested $10,000 into the business.	+10,000		+10,000	Owner investment
2. Paid $3,300 cash for three months rent.				
3. Borrowed $5,000 from the bank.				
4. Purchased furniture for $2,500 on account.				
5. Paid $700 cash for advertising.				
6. Provided services and received $2,300 cash.				
7. Paid $400 for the furniture purchased earlier.				
8. The owner withdrew $2,500 for personal use.				
9. Used up one month of rent.				

AP-5B (❺ ❻ ❼)

Nelson's Auto Repair is a new business that started operations on April 1, 2016.

Required

a) Indicate whether assets, liabilities or owner's equity will increase or decrease and by how much, based on each transaction during April. Provide an explanation only if equity is affected. The first one has been done for you. Always ensure the accounting equation is balanced.

b) Record the transactions in the T-accounts.

	Assets = Liabilities + Owner's Equity			Explanation
1. Sam invested $8,000 cash into the business.	+8,000		+8,000	Owner invested cash
2. Sam invested $2,500 of equipment into the business.				
3. Purchased tools and supplies for $6,030 on credit.				
4. Paid 12 months of insurance in advance at $250/month.				
5. Made cash sales of $4,420 during the month.				
6. Received a utility bill for $370 for the month.				
7. Paid wages to employees of $5,800.				
8. Sam withdrew $2,000 cash from the business.				
9. Recorded one month of insurance used up.				
10. Received $2,000 cash for services to be provided in two months.				

Nelson's Auto Repair
Balance Sheet
As at April 30, 2016

ASSETS

INCREASE DECREASE
+ CASH -

INCREASE DECREASE
+ PREPAID INSURANCE -

INCREASE DECREASE
+ TOOLS AND SUPPLIES -

INCREASE DECREASE
+ EQUIPMENT -

LIABILITIES

DECREASE INCREASE
- ACCOUNTS PAYABLE +

DECREASE INCREASE
- UNEARNED REVENUE +

DECREASE INCREASE
- BANK LOAN +

OWNER'S EQUITY

DECREASE INCREASE
- NELSON, CAPITAL +

INCREASE DECREASE
+ NELSON, DRAWINGS -

TOTAL ASSETS ______

TOTAL LIABILITIES ______

OWNER'S EQUITY ______ } ______

Nelson's Auto Repair
Income Statement
For the Month Ended April 30, 2016

REVENUE

DECREASE INCREASE
- SERVICE REVENUE +

LESS EXPENSES

INCREASE DECREASE
+ INSURANCE EXPENSE -

INCREASE DECREASE
+ SALARIES EXPENSE -

INCREASE DECREASE
+ UTILITIES EXPENSE -

INCREASE DECREASE

TOTAL REVENUE ______

LESS TOTAL EXPENSES ______

SURPLUS (DEFICIT) ______

c) Complete the income statement, statement of owner's equity, and balance sheet for Nelson's Auto Repair.

AP-6B (❷)

Maya's Music offers music lessons to the public for all age groups. Maya Matlin is trying to assess her business by analyzing her balance sheet. Here are the accounts and balances of Maya's Music on October 31, 2016

Accounts Payable	$1,250
Bank Loan	55,000
Building	120,000
Cash	8,150
Instruments	21,650
Prepaid Insurance	3,600
Supplies	280
Unearned Revenue	1,000

Required

Prepare the balance sheet for Maya's Music.

Analysis

Maya thinks her business must be doing great because her capital is so high. Is the balance sheet a useful tool to analyze performance? What other information would you need to be able to assess whether Maya's Music has been performing well or not? Explain.

____

____

____

____

____

____

____

____

AP-7B (❸ ❺ ❻ ❼)

Brenda Darby recently started her own consulting business, and completed these transactions during the first month of operations (May 2016)

1. Brenda invested $10,700 cash in the business.
2. Purchased store furniture for $4,000 cash.
3. Paid $1,100 cash for two months of insurance in advance.
4. Incurred business registration expenses, paid with $640 cash.
5. Paid travel expenses with $1,200 cash.
6. Received $2,300 cash from clients for consulting services provided during the month.
7. Borrowed $3,800 cash from the bank.
8. Paid salary to an assistant with $790 cash.
9. Received bills of $900 for May's electricity, water and telephone, to be paid next month.
10. Brenda withdrew $700 cash for personal purposes.
11. Received $1,000 cash for a consulting service to be completed next month.

Required

Record the above transactions in the T-account worksheet.

Brenda's Shoe Repair
Balance Sheet
As at May 31, 2016

ASSETS

INCREASE DECREASE
\+ **CASH** -

INCREASE DECREASE
\+ **PREPAID INSURANCE** -

INCREASE DECREASE
\+ **FURNITURE** -

LIABILITIES

DECREASE INCREASE
\- **ACCOUNTS PAYABLE** +

DECREASE INCREASE
\- **UNEARNED REVENUE** +

DECREASE INCREASE
\- **BANK LOAN** +

OWNER'S EQUITY

DECREASE INCREASE
\- **DARBY, CAPITAL** +

INCREASE DECREASE
\+ **DARBY, DRAWINGS** -

TOTAL ASSETS ______
TOTAL LIABILITIES ______
OWNER'S EQUITY ______ } ______

Brenda's Shoe Repair
Income Statement
For the Month Ended May 31, 2016

REVENUE

DECREASE INCREASE
\- **SERVICE REVENUE** +

LESS EXPENSES

INCREASE DECREASE
\+ **REGISTRATION EXPENSE** -

INCREASE DECREASE
\+ **SALARIES EXPENSE** -

INCREASE DECREASE
\+ **TRAVEL EXPENSE** -

INCREASE DECREASE
\+ **UTILITIES EXPENSE** -

TOTAL REVENUE ______
LESS TOTAL EXPENSES ______
NET INCOME (LOSS) ______

AP-8B (❸ ❺ ❻ ❼)

Deep Drains is a plumbing company that started operations in February 2015. The company is fully owned by Emma Reno. Consider the following opening balances as of February 1, 2016.

Cash	$13,200
Prepaid Rent	5,700
Prepaid Insurance	4,000
Property, Plant & Equipment	38,200
Accounts Payable	3,300
Bank Loan	11,300
Reno, Capital	46,500

The following transactions were completed during the month of February

1. Purchased plane tickets for business travel with $1,140 cash.
2. Paid $3,300 cash to reduce the balance of accounts payable.
3. Purchased equipment worth $3,400 with a bank loan.
4. The owner invested $6,700 additional cash in the company.
5. Paid $850 cash for registration expenses.
6. Received a bill for $590 for utilities used during the month. The bill was immediately paid with cash.
7. Earned revenue and received $10,000 cash.
8. Recognized prepaid rent as an expense for $1,110.
9. Paid interest for the month of February with $50 cash.
10. Paid monthly salaries with for $4,100 cash.
11. The owner withdrew $2,500 cash from the business to pay for personal expenses.
12. Received $2,000 cash in advance for services to be rendered in three months.

Required

a) Using the information provided, record the opening balances in the T-accounts.

b) Record the transactions for the month of February in the T-accounts.

Deep Drains
Balance Sheet
As at February 29, 2016

ASSETS

INCREASE DECREASE
+ **CASH** -
Opening

INCREASE DECREASE
+ **PREPAID RENT** -
Opening

INCREASE DECREASE
+ **PREPAID INSURANCE** -
Opening

INCREASE DECREASE
+ **EQUIPMENT** -
Opening

LIABILITIES

DECREASE INCREASE
- **ACCOUNTS PAYABLE** +
Opening

DECREASE INCREASE
- **UNEARNED REVENUE** +
Opening

DECREASE INCREASE
- **BANK LOAN** +
Opening

OWNER'S EQUITY

DECREASE INCREASE
- **RENO, CAPITAL** +
Opening

INCREASE DECREASE
+ **RENO, DRAWINGS** -

TOTAL ASSETS ________
TOTAL LIABILITIES ________
OWNER'S EQUITY ________ } ________

Deep Drains
Income Statement
For the Month Ended February 29, 2016

REVENUE

DECREASE INCREASE
- **SERVICE REVENUE** +

LESS EXPENSES

INCREASE DECREASE
+ **INTEREST EXPENSE** -

INCREASE DECREASE
+ **REGISTRATION EXPENSE** -

INCREASE DECREASE
+ **RENT EXPENSE** -

INCREASE DECREASE
+ **SALARIES EXPENSE** -

INCREASE DECREASE
+ **TELEPHONE & UTILITIES EXPENSE** -

INCREASE DECREASE
+ **TRAVEL EXPENSE** -

TOTAL REVENUE ________
LESS TOTAL EXPENSES ________
NET INCOME (LOSS) ________

AP-9B (❸ ❺ ❻ ❼)

Candace Harris Legal is a law firm. On July 31, 2016, the firm had the following ending balances

Cash	$18,500
Prepaid Insurance	9,200
Property, Plant & Equipment	22,300
Accounts Payable	8,100
Harris, Capital	41,900

During the month of August, the company completed the following transactions

1. Purchased $1,000 of office equipment on account.
2. Received $4,600 cash from customers for services rendered.
3. Paid $4,900 owing to a supplier.
4. Paid $570 utilities bill for August with cash.
5. Purchased a computer on account for $1,420.
6. Paid August's salaries with $3,600 cash.
7. Received a $1,150 bill to be paid in September for advertisements placed in a national newspaper during the month of August to promote Candace Harris Legal.
8. Performed services worth of $2,000 for customers on account.
9. Withdrew $3,200 cash for personal use.
10. Recognized $1,700 insurance for August (which was previously prepaid).
11. Received $1,500 cash for legal services to be done next month.
12. Collected all the balances owing from customers for services performed earlier.

Required

a) Using the information provided, record the opening balances in the T-accounts.

b) Record the transactions for the month of August in the T-accounts.

Candace Harris Legal
Balance Sheet
As at August 31, 2016

ASSETS

INCREASE DECREASE
+ **CASH** -
Opening

INCREASE DECREASE
+ **ACCOUNTS RECEIVABLE** -
Opening

INCREASE DECREASE
+ **PREPAID INSURANCE** -
Opening

INCREASE DECREASE
+ **EQUIPMENT** -
Opening

LIABILITIES

DECREASE INCREASE
- **ACCOUNTS PAYABLE** +
Opening

DECREASE INCREASE
- **UNEARNED REVENUE** +
Opening

OWNER'S EQUITY

DECREASE INCREASE
- **HARRIS, CAPITAL** +
Opening

INCREASE DECREASE
+ **HARRIS, DRAWINGS** -

TOTAL ASSETS ______

TOTAL LIABILITIES ______

OWNER'S EQUITY ______

Candace Harris Legal
Income Statement
For the Month Ended August 31, 2016

REVENUE

DECREASE INCREASE
- **SERVICE REVENUE** +

LESS EXPENSES

INCREASE DECREASE
+ **ADVERTISING EXPENSE** -

INCREASE DECREASE
+ **INSURANCE EXPENSE** -

INCREASE DECREASE
+ **SALARIES EXPENSE** -

INCREASE DECREASE
+ **UTILITIES EXPENSE** -

TOTAL REVENUE ______

LESS TOTAL EXPENSES ______

NET INCOME (LOSS) ______

AP-10B (❸ ❺ ❻ ❼)

Christine Jacob is a financial planning consultant. During the month of February 2016, she completed the following transactions

1. Christine invested $8,000 cash in the business.
2. Paid $1,400 cash for February office rent.
3. Received $6,500 from a client for services rendered.
4. Paid $500 cash to Shell Super Service for gas purchases.
5. Paid $700 cash to Helpful Manpower Services for consulting services.
6. Purchased office equipment worth $900 on account.
7. Owner withdrew $2,500 cash for personal use.
8. Donated $800 cash to the National Red Cross.
9. Provided $2,000 worth of services for a client who paid on account.
10. Made partial payment of $500 on the equipment that was purchased on account.
11. Received $500 cash for services to be provided next month.
12. Collected $1,000 cash from a client who owed for services provided earlier in the month.

Required

Prepare the T-account worksheet.

Christine Jacob Financial Planning
Balance Sheet
As at February 29, 2016

ASSETS

INCREASE +	DECREASE -
Opening	

INCREASE +	DECREASE -
Opening	

INCREASE +	DECREASE -
Opening	

LIABILITIES

DECREASE -	INCREASE +
	Opening

DECREASE -	INCREASE +
	Opening

OWNER'S EQUITY

DECREASE -	INCREASE +
	Opening

INCREASE +	DECREASE -

TOTAL ASSETS ______

TOTAL LIABILITIES ______ } ______

OWNER'S EQUITY ______

Christine Jacob Financial Planning
Income Statement
For the Month Ended February 29, 2016

REVENUE

DECREASE -	INCREASE +

LESS EXPENSES

INCREASE +	DECREASE -

INCREASE +	DECREASE -

INCREASE +	DECREASE -

INCREASE +	DECREASE -

INCREASE	DECREASE

TOTAL REVENUE ______

LESS TOTAL EXPENSES ______

NET INCOME (LOSS) ______

AP-11B (❸ ❺ ❻ ❼)

Troy Dale, an architect, opened his own business on March 1, 2016. During the month, he completed the following transactions related to his professional practice

1. Transferred $30,000 cash from personal bank account to the business account.
2. Provided services for $3,000 cash.
3. Purchased office and computer equipment worth $8,000 on account, which will be paid next month.
4. Paid $1,100 cash for meals and entertainment.
5. Paid insurance expense with $800 cash.
6. Performed services for clients for $4,000 on account.
7. Paid $600 cash for miscellaneous expenses.
8. Received utilities bill of $1,000, to be paid next month.
9. Paid $1,200 cash for office rent for the month of March.
10. Paid $1,000 salary to assistant.
11. Collected 50% of the balance owing from clients for services performed earlier this month.
12. Received $1,000 cash for services to be performed in three months.

Required

Prepare the T-account worksheet.

Dale Architect
Balance Sheet
As at March 31, 2016

ASSETS

INCREASE +	DECREASE -
Opening	

INCREASE +	DECREASE -
Opening	

INCREASE +	DECREASE -
Opening	

LIABILITIES

DECREASE -	INCREASE +
	Opening

DECREASE -	INCREASE +
	Opening

OWNER'S EQUITY

DECREASE -	INCREASE +
	Opening

INCREASE +	DECREASE -

TOTAL ASSETS ________

TOTAL LIABILITIES ________ } ________

OWNER'S EQUITY ________

Dale Architect
Income Statement
For the Month Ended March 31, 2016

REVENUE

DECREASE -	INCREASE +

LESS EXPENSES

INCREASE +	DECREASE -

INCREASE +	DECREASE -

INCREASE +	DECREASE -

INCREASE +	DECREASE -

INCREASE +	DECREASE -

INCREASE +	DECREASE -

TOTAL REVENUE ________

LESS TOTAL EXPENSES ________

NET INCOME (LOSS) ________

AP-12B (❷ ❸ ❺ ❻ ❼)

Ella Kates founded Health-Plus Clinic as a medical clinic that started operations in January 2015. Consider the following opening balances as of January 1, 2016.

Cash	$15,000
Prepaid Rent	6,000
Prepaid Insurance	5,000
Equipment	30,000
Accounts Payable	3,000
Bank Loan	10,000
Kates, Capital	43,000

Transactions during the month of January

1. Purchased plane tickets with $1,500 cash. The plane tickets are to attend a business conference.
2. Paid $3,000 cash to reduce the balance of accounts payable.
3. The owner invested $5,000 additional cash in the company.
4. Purchased $4,000 worth of equipment with a bank loan.
5. Paid $1,000 cash for maintenance expenses.
6. Earned $15,000 revenue from patients on a cash basis.
7. Received a $900 bill for utilities used during the month. A cheque was issued to pay the bill immediately.
8. Recognized $2,000 of prepaid rent as an expense.
9. Paid $100 interest for the month with cash.
10. Paid $4,000 monthly salaries to all medical practitioners and clinic personnel.
11. Received $2,000 cash from one of its clients for services to be provided in March.
12. The owner withdrew $2,000 cash from the business to pay for personal expenses.

Required

Prepare the T-account worksheet, income statement, statement of owner's equity, and balance sheet.

Health-Plus Clinic
Balance Sheet
As at January 31, 2016

ASSETS

INCREASE | DECREASE
+ | -
Opening

INCREASE | DECREASE
+ | -
Opening

INCREASE | DECREASE
+ | -
Opening

INCREASE | DECREASE
+ | -
Opening

LIABILITIES

DECREASE | INCREASE
- | +
Opening

DECREASE | INCREASE
- | +
Opening

DECREASE | INCREASE
- | +
Opening

OWNER'S EQUITY

DECREASE | INCREASE
- | +
Opening

INCREASE | DECREASE
+ | -

TOTAL ASSETS ________

TOTAL LIABILITIES ________

OWNER'S EQUITY ________ } ________

Health-Plus Clinic
Income Statement
For the Month Ended January 31, 2016

REVENUE

DECREASE | INCREASE
- | +

LESS EXPENSES

INCREASE | DECREASE
+ | -

INCREASE | DECREASE
+ | -

INCREASE | DECREASE
+ | -

INCREASE | DECREASE
+ | -

INCREASE | DECREASE
+ | -

INCREASE | DECREASE
+ | -

TOTAL REVENUE ________

LESS TOTAL EXPENSES ________

NET INCOME (LOSS) ________

Health-Plus Clinic
Income Statement
For the Month Ended January 31, 2016

Health-Plus Clinic
Statement of Owner's Equity
For the Month Ended January 31, 2016

Health-Plus Clinic
Balance Sheet
As at January 31, 2016

AP-13B (❷ ❸ ❺ ❻ ❼)

Helga Stiles operates a hairstyling company. The opening balances from Helga's Hairstyling's financial records on March 1, 2016 is shown below.

Cash	$18,000
Equipment	4,300
Supplies	1,200
Building	140,000
Accounts Payable	3,600
Bank Loan	100,000
Stiles, Capital	59,900

The following transactions took place during the month of March

1. $5,000 cash was taken from the bank account for a bank loan payment.
2. Paid down a portion of the accounts payable with $1,000 cash.
3. Recorded cash sales of $5,500.
4. Received a delivery of supplies for $2,000; invoice due in 30 days.
5. Received a bill of $650 for maintenance on equipment.
6. Paid salaries to employees with $1,500 cash.
7. Withdrew $2,000 cash from the business.
8. Provided services worth $2,000 for clients on account.
9. Received $1,500 cash in advance of service to be done next month.
10. Collected $1,000 of the amount owing from clients.

Required

a) Record the transactions in the T-accounts.

Helga's Hairstyling
Balance Sheet
As at March 31, 2016

ASSETS

INCREASE	DECREASE
+ **CASH**	-
Opening	

INCREASE	DECREASE
- **ACCOUNTS RECEIVABLE**	+
Opening	

INCREASE	DECREASE
+ **SUPPLIES**	-
Opening	

INCREASE	DECREASE
+ **EQUIPMENT**	-
Opening	

INCREASE	DECREASE
+ **BUILDING**	-
Opening	

LIABILITIES

DECREASE	INCREASE
- **ACCOUNTS PAYABLE**	+
	Opening

DECREASE	INCREASE
- **UNEARNED REVENUE**	+
	Opening

DECREASE	INCREASE
- **BANK LOAN**	+
	Opening

OWNER'S EQUITY

DECREASE	INCREASE
- **STILES, CAPITAL**	+
	Opening

INCREASE	DECREASE
+ **STILES, DRAWINGS**	-

TOTAL ASSETS ______

TOTAL LIABILITIES ______ } ______

OWNER'S EQUITY ______

Helga's Hairstyling
Income Statement
For the Month Ended March 31, 2016

REVENUE

DECREASE	INCREASE
- **SERVICE REVENUE**	+

LESS EXPENSES

INCREASE	DECREASE
+ **MAINTENANCE EXPENSE**	-

INCREASE	DECREASE
+ **SALARIES EXPENSE**	-

INCREASE	DECREASE
+ **TELEPHONE EXPENSE**	-

INCREASE	DECREASE
+ **UTILITIES EXPENSE**	-

TOTAL REVENUE ______

LESS TOTAL EXPENSES ______

NET INCOME (LOSS) ______

b) Complete the Income Statement, Statement of Owner's Equity, and Balance Sheet for the end of March 2016.

AP-14B (❷)

Jake Martin operates a construction company as a sole proprietorship called Martin & Martin Construction. Jake is creating some financial records for the company for the end of April 2016 and has come up with the following account balances.

Accounts Payable	$750
Accounts Receivable	350
Bank Loan	5,000
Cash	11,250
Storage Warehouse	36,200
Tools and Equipment	7,900
Vehicle	13,800

Required

Prepare the balance sheet for Martin and Martin Construction.

Case Study

CS-1 (❸❺❻❼)

Granyard Clockworks is a service company that repairs damaged watches and clocks. The company is owned fully by John Granyard. John is fully liable for all activities of the business. In the most recent month (May 2016), Granyard Clockworks had the following transactions

1. John deposited $40,000 of additional cash into the business.
2. Borrowed $15,000 in cash from the bank.
3. Paid $3,500 cash for May's rent.
4. Paid $6,000 in salaries for May.
5. Performed services and earned $18,000 in cash.
6. Incurred telephone expenses of $500 (to be paid next month).
7. Performed services for a client for $3,000 on account.
8. Prepaid insurance for one year in the amount of $11,000.
9. Incurred maintenance expense of $1,000 (paid on account).
10. John withdrew $5,000 from the business for personal use.
11. Received $2,000 cash for repair services to be done in July.
12. Collected 80% of the $3,000 amount owing from a client for services performed earlier this month.

As at April 30, 2016, the ending account balances for Granyard Clockworks were

Cash	$50,000
Accounts Receivable	12,000
Prepaid Insurance	800
Equipment	40,000
Accounts Payable	2,000
Bank Loan	60,000
Granyard, Capital	40,800

Required

a) Complete the T-account worksheets for May 2016 (provided below).

Granyard Clockworks
Balance Sheet
As at May 31, 2016

ASSETS

INCREASE DECREASE
+ **CASH** -
Opening

INCREASE DECREASE
- **ACCOUNTS RECEIVABLE** +
Opening

INCREASE DECREASE
+ **PREPAID INSURANCE** -
Opening

INCREASE DECREASE
+ **EQUIPMENT** -
Opening

LIABILITIES

DECREASE INCREASE
- **ACCOUNTS PAYABLE** +
Opening

DECREASE INCREASE
- **UNEARNED REVENUE** +
Opening

DECREASE INCREASE
- **BANK LOAN** +
Opening

OWNER'S EQUITY

DECREASE INCREASE
- **GRANYARD, CAPITAL** +
Opening

INCREASE DECREASE
+ **GRANYARD, DRAWINGS** -

TOTAL ASSETS ______
TOTAL LIABILITIES ______
OWNER'S EQUITY ______

Granyard Clockworks
Income Statement
For the Month Ended May 31, 2016

REVENUE

DECREASE INCREASE
- **REVENUE** +

LESS EXPENSES

INCREASE DECREASE
+ **MAINTENANCE EXPENSE** -

INCREASE DECREASE
+ **RENT EXPENSE** -

INCREASE DECREASE
+ **SALARIES EXPENSE** -

INCREASE DECREASE
+ **TELEPHONE EXPENSE** -

INCREASE DECREASE

TOTAL REVENUE ______
LESS TOTAL EXPENSES ______
NET INCOME (LOSS) ______

b) If John Granyard were to sell all of the assets of the business for cash on May 31, 2016 and use the cash to pay off the company's debts, what is the remaining amount? What does it represent?

Chapter 3

THE ACCOUNTING FRAMEWORK

LEARNING OUTCOMES

1. Describe the users of accounting information
2. Describe the fields of accounting
3. Compare the different forms of business organization
4. Discuss the qualitative characteristics of financial information
5. List and apply basic accounting assumptions and principles
6. Illustrate the similarities and differences between ASPE and IFRS
7. Explain the importance of ethics in accounting

AMEENGAGE™ *Access **ameengage.com** for integrated resources including tutorials, practice exercises, the digital textbook and more.*

Assessment Questions

AS-1 (❶)

What is an internal user? What do internal users use financial information for?

AS-2 (❶)

What is an external user? What do external users use financial information for?

AS-3 (❷)

Briefly define financial accounting.

AS-4 (❷)

Briefly define managerial accounting.

AS-5 (❸)

What is a sole proprietorship? What is the title of a sole proprietorship's equity section?

AS-6 (❸)

Explain the concept of unlimited liability.

AS-7 (❸)

What is a partnership?

AS-8 (❸)

What are the three types of partnerships that can be created?

AS-9 (❸)

What is the difference between a general partnership and a limited partnership?

AS-10 (❸)

Describe a corporation.

AS-11 (❸)

What is a not-for-profit organization?

AS-12 (❸)

Provide three examples of not-for-profit organizations.

AS-13 (❹ ❻)

Briefly define and explain GAAP. What are the two frameworks that have evolved from Canadian GAAP?

AS-14 (❹)

What are the four qualitative characteristics of effective and useful information?

AS-15 (❹)

Describe the characteristic of relevance.

AS-16 (❹)

Describe timeliness. Which characteristic is timeliness a component of?

AS-17 (❹)

Describe the characteristic of reliability.

AS-18 (❹)

What is verifiability? Which characteristic is verifiability a component of?

AS-19 (❹)

What is conservatism? Which characteristic is conservatism a component of?

AS-20 (❹)

Describe the characteristic of understandability.

AS-21 (❹)

What is representational faithfulness? Which characteristic is representational faithfulness a component of?

AS-22 (❹)

What is neutrality? Neutrality is a component of which characteristic?

AS-23 (❹)

Describe the characteristic of comparability.

AS-24 (❹)

What is a trade-off? Provide an example of a commonly discussed trade-off of qualitative characteristics.

AS-25 (❺)

Describe the business entity assumption.

AS-26 (❺)

Describe the going concern assumption.

AS-27 (❺)

Describe the monetary unit assumption.

AS-28 (❺)

Describe the principle of measurement.

AS-29 (❺)

Describe the time period concept.

AS-30 (❺)

Describe the principle of revenue recognition.

AS-31 (❺)

Describe the principle of expense recognition.

AS-32 (❺)

Describe the principle of consistency.

AS-33 (❺)

Describe the principle of materiality.

AS-34 (❺)

Describe the principle of disclosure.

AS-35 (❻)

What is ASPE and which forms of organization can adhere to it?

AS-36 (❻)

What is IFRS and which forms of organization can adhere to it?

____

____

____

____

AS-37 (❼)

List two ethical standards for accountants.

____

____

____

____

Application Questions Group A

AP-1A (❸)

Match each form of an organization with the appropriate description.

A	Sole proprietorship
B	Partnership
C	Corporation
D	Not-for-Profit Organization

____	This type of organization usually does not have an identifiable owner.
____	There are two types: one that limits the liability of the owners and one that does not.
____	A business operated by a single owner.
____	This type of business often elects a board of directors.

AP-2A (❹ ❺)

Match each of the following basic ASPE and IFRS concepts and principles to the appropriate description in the table below.

- Business entity assumption
- Going concern assumption
- Monetary unit assumption
- Revenue recognition
- Measurement
- Conservatism

Term (fill in)	**Description**
	The accountant should exercise the option that results in a lower balance of assets, lower net income or a higher balance of debt.
	Sales must be recorded when ownership of a good transfers from the seller to the buyer.
	Assumes that a business will continue to operate into the foreseeable future.
	Financial reports should be expressed in a single currency.
	Accounting for a business must be kept separate from the personal affairs of its owner or any other business.
	Purchases must be recorded at their values on the date of purchase.

AP-3A (❹)

Hawkton Publishing Corporation is a publisher of math textbooks. The company is a large, well-known publicly traded corporation with thousands of shareholders. It produces financial statements on an annual basis. The most recent financial statements (for the year ended December 31, 2016) showed comparative balances for 2016 and 2015. The 2016 balances were derived using accrual-based accounting whereas the 2015 balances were derived using cash-based accounting.

Which characteristic(s) of information did Hawkton fail to represent? Explain.

AP-4A (❺)

Alton Floral is a new company that operates in the gardening industry. The owner of the company has decided not to hire an accountant but instead maintain the accounting records on his own. He has included his employees as assets on the balance sheet in the account "Human Resources." He has valued them at the present value of their future salaries on the balance sheet. Also, the financial statements are not supported by notes explaining some of the figures.

Which of the basic accounting principles and/or assumptions has Alton Floral violated? Explain.

AP-5A (❺)

Suppose that a company has changed its policy for depreciation from one year to the next. An employee in the accounting department addressed this change with the owner. The employee asked the owner why the accounting policy was changed and why the reasoning for the change was not disclosed in the financial statements. The owner replied, "IFRS gives you the option to use a different depreciation method from one year to the next. We also are not required to explain our choices." Is the owner correct in his reasoning? Explain.

AP-6A (❺)

Heggy Company, a privately owned corporation, is producing cellphone accessories. It relies on ASPE to prepare its financial statements. The company is doing well and is planning to expand its product line. Assume you are a newly hired accountant for Heggy and you are reviewing the company's financial statements.

You realize that the company recently purchased machinery for $700,000 as part of its expansion strategy. After a long negotiation, Heggy's purchasing department was able to find the best deal which was well below the market value of $740,000. The machinery has been recorded in Heggy's books at $740,000.

Also, Heggy Company has paid $15,000 for the cost of the plant's insurance for the upcoming year and expensed the whole amount. Heggy believes that this expensing would be an effective cost-saving strategy in the long run as it will avoid the extra bookkeeping associated with updating the prepaid insurance account.

Has Heggy Company violated any of the basic concepts and principles of ASPE? Explain.

AP-7A (❺)

Tasai Corporation is a Canadian manufacturer of wings for commercial aircrafts. Tasai is a large public company which is famous for the unique design of its wings. You are appointed as its audit manager.

As you go through the financial statements you notice, on the income statement, the company has set aside one line item under revenue which shows an amount of 800,000 in Brazilian currency (reals). In the notes related to this item, it is indicated that the company has completed a project in Brazil; and due to the large amount of foreign exchange loss, the company has decided to report the figure in reals. The accounting department thinks this practice is permitted under IFRS as long as it is clearly explained in the notes.

You also note this year's travel expense is significantly larger than last year's. As part of the audit procedures, you examine travel documents and invoices and realize that one of the owners included his personal travel expenses as part of his business-related travels. In addition, Tasai Corporation has changed one of its accounting policies and disclosed the nature, impact and reason of this change in the notes.

As the audit manager, discuss if any accounting assumptions or principles have been violated.

AP-8A (❹ ❺)

Sood Supplies is in the business of selling electronic components to computer manufacturers. Sood Supplies' financial statements are issued on an annual basis for a large number of users such as investors and the bank. The financial reporting of the company is based on ASPE.

Prior to the issuance of the current year's financial statements, the head of engineering and the accounting manager had a discussion regarding the amount of warranty expense that should be recognized for the year. The head of engineering believes that only 2% of sales needs to be calculated as a provision for the warranty expense while the accounting manager believes that 6% of sales should be recorded as an expense. The accounting manager argues that the 6% is estimated based on historical trends of the company and the industry; however, the engineering department claims that its new method of quality assurance will reduce the future warranty expenses.The engineering department could not submit any documents to support the claim. Eventually, the accounting manager decides to trust the engineering department and uses the 2% calculation.

Do you believe any of the accounting principles or qualitative characteristics have been violated by Sood Supplies? Explain.

AP-9A (❹)

Identify the qualitative characteristic of financial information that has been violated in each of the following scenarios.

a) Thorn Company has reported several gains for the period, but has not provided any explanation or proof of how they occurred.

b) Due to recent layoffs, Monte Carlo Ltd. was not able to complete and issue its 2015 financial statements and accompanying notes. The information was instead included with the 2016 financial report in the following year.

____

c) To value inventory, Toland and Sons uses a different accounting policy from the rest of the companies in the same industry. There is no justification for the use of this accounting policy in the notes to the financial statements.

____

d) Eris Laboratories used many uncommon medical terms and scientific language in the notes to the financial statements. This language was not explained anywhere else.

____

e) A bank decided not to grant a loan to Mida Ltd. after a customer filed a substantial lawsuit. Mida Ltd. did not include any mention of the lawsuit in the financial statements or in the notes to the financial statements.

____

AP-10A (❺)

Identify the accounting principle or concept that has been violated in each of the following scenarios.

a) Bill Co. purchased a two-year insurance policy and expensed the entire amount in period of purchase.

____

b) Charlie Co. listed inventory at its market value of $31,000 on the balance sheet, even though it was purchased for $20,000.

____

c) Percy Co. did not include the details of its property, plant, and equipment, even though this information is relevant to the users.

____

d) Fred Co. made a sale on the last day of the accounting period. The customer paid for the item in the following month, so this sale was included in the next period's financial statements.

____

e) George Co. has plans to restructure its operations next year and will sell off about half of the business. This information was not included in the notes to the financial statements because it does not affect the current financial information.

____

f) Ron Co. applied a certain accounting policy which allowed the company to report higher assets and net income. A different accounting policy was available which would have resulted in a lower balance of assets and net income.

____

g) Ginny Co. changed the accounting policy used to value property, plant, and equipment after using a different policy for 10 years. There was no justification for the change.

____

AP-11A (❹ ❺)

For each accounting principle or assumption, indicate which one of the four characteristics of information it is most related to.

Characteristic (fill in)	**Basic Concept or Principle**
	Monetary Unit Assumption
	Objectivity Principle
	Measurement
	Consistency
	Materiality
	Disclosure

AP-12A (❻)

Heath Trek Company has four different asset accounts: property, plant & equipment, accounts receivable, short-term investments and cash. Shown below is the average amount of time required to turn each asset into cash.

Asset	Cash Turnover Time (in days)
Property, plant & equipment	5,480
Accounts receivable	60
Short-term investments	120
Cash	N/A

Required

a) If Heath Trek's financial statements were prepared using ASPE, in which order will the assets be presented on the balance sheet?

b) If Heath Trek's financial statements were prepared using IFRS instead, in which order will the assets be presented on the balance sheet?

AP-13A (❼)

Joan is a senior accountant who recently agreed to give a professional review of the financial statements of Baker Consulting Inc. Joan is a personal friend of the president of this company and has an outstanding loan to the company. Baker Consulting Inc. is having cash flow issues which may force it to lay off some employees, but the owner has assured Joan that everything is under control and that the company is about to land several large sales contracts. He also explained that if the financial statements revealed any issues, the company would lose potential customers and suppliers. After some discussion, Joan decided to issue a positive opinion of the financial statements and not disclose any issues. Has Joan violated any ethical standards of accounting? Discuss.

Application Questions Group B

AP-1B (❹)

Match each of the following characteristics of financial information to the appropriate description in the table below.

- Relevance
- Reliability
- Understandability
- Comparability
- Timeliness
- Verifiability

Term (fill in)	**Description**
	Information is free from material error and bias
	A component of relevance
	The financial statements of a company should be prepared in a similar way year after year
	A component of reliability
	Financial information can be comprehended by users with a reasonable knowledge of the business
	All information for decision making is present in the financial statements

AP-2B (❺)

Match each of the following basic concepts and principles to the appropriate description in the table below.

- Time period concept
- Expense recognition
- Consistency
- Materiality
- Disclosure

Term (fill in)	**Description**
	Accounting takes place over specific fiscal periods.
	Prevents people from changing accounting methods for the sole purpose of manipulating figures on the financial statements.
	The costs of doing business must be recorded in (or matched to) the same accounting period as the revenues which they helped to generate.
	Any and all information that affects the full understanding of a company's financial statements must be included with the financial statements.
	This refers to the significance of information to users. The more significant a piece of information is means that it could influence or change a user's decision.

AP-3B (④)

Reflex Sports Inc. is a manufacturer of sports equipment for children. It relies on IFRS to prepare its financial statements. The nature of its accounting transactions can be quite complex at times. However, the financial statements have no additional notes to support them. The company also does not keep all invoices on record to back up expense amounts reported on the financial statements. Which characteristic(s) of information did Reflex Sports fail to represent? Explain.

____

____

____

____

____

AP-4B (⑤)

Mackenzie Attire is currently preparing its annual financial statements for the past fiscal year. The company uses cash-based accounting. The company's policy includes receiving payment for its services well before the service is performed. The owner recently purchased a fish tank for his home and the transaction included a decrease to Mackenzie Attire's equity (an expense was recorded in the income statement). The value of inventory is adjusted annually to be stated at fair value. Which of the basic accounting principles and/or assumptions has Mackenzie Attire violated? Explain.

____

____

____

____

____

____

____

____

____

AP-5B (❺)

IMORI is large publicly traded construction company. IMORI has entered into a three-year construction contract with Siano Company. Siano paid upfront for the full value of the contract, and IMORI has recorded the entire amount as revenue immediately. Explain the accounting principle that has been violated.

AP-6B (❺)

Blossoma Inc. is a private supplier of organic beauty products. The company prepares its financial statements in compliance with ASPE. Due to recent economic difficulties, Blossoma Inc. had to file for bankruptcy. The company's property, plant and equipment are listed on the balance sheet at what they could be sold for, which is lower than their original purchase price. Has Blossoma Inc. violated any of the basic accounting principles and/or assumptions? Explain.

AP-7B (❹ ❺)

Team Toro Inc , a unionized company, is in the business of planning and hosting events for various colleges and universities. Its service includes a wide range of activities such as decor and design, accommodation for guests, and catering. At the end of the year, prior to issuance of its financial statements, the head of the accounting department realized that the union was not able to negotiate a collective agreement with the board and it is planning to go on strike legally at the beginning of next year. After discussing the matter with the board members, the accounting manager decides not to disclose this issue since the strike will happen next year and this year's financial statements are not affected. In addition, the accounting manager thinks the disclosure may have an unnecessarily negative impact on the company's financial position and reputation in the market. Discuss whether any accounting principles or qualitative characteristics have been violated.

AP-8B (❹ ❺)

Imzy Company is a small private company that relies on ASPE to prepare financial statements. During the year, the company has experienced a number of tax disputes with the government. This issue was not included in the notes to the financial statements as the bookkeeper believes this type of tax dispute is common for a small business. In addition, the bookkeeper does not keep purchase invoices because he thinks the costs of holding all those receipts would outweigh their benefits for a small company. Explain whether any accounting principles or qualitative characteristics have been violated by the bookkeeper.

AP-9B (❹)

Identify the qualitative characteristic that describes each of the following scenarios.

a) Titus Group presented its financial information in a way that allowed informed users to comprehend the meaning of the information.

b) Hunt Manufacturing included references to source documents to explain where certain financial figures originated from.

c) Arloc Games Company uses the same accounting methods each year when preparing the financial statements.

d) Crypt Technologies reported all financial information that could have an impact on the decisions of the users of the financial statements.

AP-10B (❺)

Identify the accounting principle that describes each of the following scenarios.

a) Pangea Construction recorded revenue for a five-year construction contract evenly over the five years.

____

b) Athena Spa has committed to opening a second location in the next eight months. Details regarding this expansion were included in the financial information.

____

c) Zeus Electric used the same accounting policy for depreciation as last year, even though it could have reported a higher net income by switching to a different method.

____

d) Neptune Water Supply grouped small assets such as pens, staplers, and notepads together as office supplies because the cost of separating them outweighed the benefits.

____

e) Hermes Athletics had its land appraised at $60,000. The land was listed on the balance sheet at $50,000 which was the price originally paid for it.

____

f) Hera Consulting prepaid cash for its annual insurance policy. The amount was expensed on a monthly basis as it was used up.

____

AP-11B (❺ ❻)

The accountant for GYC Consultants is facing an important accounting decision. The company recently incurred a material transaction that can be accounted for in three different ways (options A, B, and C). The effect on the company's net income and total assets for each option is shown below. Under ASPE, which option should GYC's accountant choose to account for the transaction and why?

Effect on	Option A	Option B	Option C
Net Income	+$5,200	+$4,100	+$4,600
Total Assets	+$1,100	+$900	+$1,000

AP-12B (❻)

Starks Instruments Company has five different asset accounts: property, plant & equipment, inventory, cash, accounts receivable and prepaid expenses. Shown below is the level of liquidity of each asset.

Assset	Liquidity Level
Property, plant & equipment	Very low
Inventory	Medium
Cash	Very high
Accounts receivable	High
Prepaid expenses	Low

Required

a) If Starks Instruments Company's financial statements were prepared using APSE, in which order will the assets be presented on the balance sheet?

b) If Starks Instruments Company's financial statements were prepared using IFRS instead, in which order will the assets be presented on the balance sheet?

____

____

____

AP-13B (❼)

Marcus is the senior accountant for a small accounting firm. He is currently performing the year-end audit of a particular client: Le Jardin Oak Inc. (LJO), a manufacturer of high quality furniture. After Marcus met with Le Jardin's CEO in a restaurant, the CEO noticed that Le Jardin's financial records, which were provided to Marcus, were scattered on the ground. The CEO was extremely disappointed because the records were meant for internal use only. Which ethical standard did Marcus violate? Explain.

____

____

____

____

____

Case Study

CS-1 (❹ ❺)

Gordon is the majority owner of Gordon House Restaurant (GHR), a publicly traded chain of family restaurants. The company is owned by hundreds of shareholders who expect timely, reliable and accurate financial statements. GHR produces financial statements periodically. It is now June 15, 2016. The accountant has prepared the financial statements for the eight-month period ended May 31, 2016. The previous financial statements covered a one-year period.

GHR was recently sued by another company, the details of which are not disclosed in the financial statements. The court proceedings have not yet ended. However, as of May 31, 2016, it was believed that GHR is very likely to lose the case and eventually pay a significant amount in damages to the plaintiff.

Also consider the following additional information:

- Cash disbursements are not supported by additional source documents
- GHR has recognized revenue in a different accounting period than the costs associated with producing that revenue

Required

a) Which of the four qualitative characteristics of financial information has GHR failed to apply? Explain.

b) Which of the basic concepts and principles of accounting has GHR violated? Explain.

Chapter 4

THE ACCOUNTING CYCLE: JOURNALS AND LEDGERS

LEARNING OUTCOMES

❶ Distinguish between debits and credits
❷ Describe the accounting cycle
❸ Explain how to analyze a transaction
❹ Record transactions in the general journal
❺ Post journal entries to the general ledger
❻ Prepare a trial balance

AMEENGAGE™ *Access **ameengage.com** for integrated resources including tutorials, practice exercises, the digital textbook and more.*

Assessment Questions

AS-1 (❶)

What does the term debit refer to?

____

____

AS-2 (❶)

True or False: A credit will always be an increase to any account.

____

____

AS-3 (❶)

Which three types of accounts use the debit side of the T-account to increase their value?

____

____

AS-4 (❶)

Which three types of accounts use the credit side of the T-account to increase their value?

____

____

AS-5 (❶)

What is the normal balance of an asset?

AS-6 (❶)

What is the normal balance of a liability?

AS-7 (❹)

Explain the purpose of a chart of accounts.

AS-8 (❷ ❸ ❹ ❺ ❻)

List and describe the first four steps of the accounting cycle.

AS-9 (❹)

In the accounting cycle, what is the purpose of creating journals?

AS-10 (❺)

In the accounting cycle, what is the purpose of the general ledger?

___

AS-11 (❻)

In the accounting cycle, what is the purpose of the trial balance?

___

AS-12 (❹)

In the journal, what information will be entered in the PR (posting reference) column?

___

AS-13 (❺)

What is the relationship between the closing balance and the opening balance for an asset?

___

AS-14 (❻)

If the trial balance balances, were all transactions correctly recorded? Explain.

___

Application Questions Group A

AP-1A (❶ ❸)

Esteem Fitness provides fitness services for its customers. During June 2016, Esteem Fitness had the following transactions.

Jun 1 Sold one-month memberships to customers for $4,500 on account.
Jun 3 Received a telephone bill for $250 which will be paid next month.
Jun 6 Paid an employee's salary of $1,200.
Jun 10 Received $3,000 cash from customers paying in advance for upcoming one-year memberships.
Jun 15 Paid $6,000 cash in advance for six months of rent.
Jun 20 Received a $10,000 loan from the bank.
Jun 26 Purchased equipment with $8,000 cash.

Required

Complete the table to analyze each transaction.

	Account Name	Category	Increase or Decrease	Debit or Credit
Jun 1				
Jun 3				
Jun 6				
Jun 10				
Jun 15				
Jun 20				
Jun 26				

AP-2A (❶ ❸)

Have-a-Bash, owned by Finn Tymes, provides party planning services. During October 2016, Have-a-Bash had the following transactions.

Oct 1 Finn invested $5,000 cash into the business.
Oct 2 Planned a party for a customer and received $900 cash.
Oct 4 Received a $500 utilities bill which will be paid later.
Oct 10 Paid $200 cash for maintenance for the month.
Oct 12 Paid $400 towards the bank loan principal.
Oct 18 Received cash from a customer who owed $1,100.
Oct 22 Paid the utilities bill received earlier.
Oct 28 Paid $3,000 cash in advance for office rent.

Required

Complete the table to analyze each transaction.

	Account Name	Category	Increase or Decrease	Debit or Credit
Oct 1				
Oct 2				
Oct 4				
Oct 10				
Oct 12				
Oct 18				
Oct 22				
Oct 28				

AP-3A (❶)

For the following list of accounts, indicate which side of the T-account causes an increase or decrease. The first account has been done for you.

Account	Debit	Credit
Cash	Increase	Decrease
Advertising Expense		
Service Revenue		
Unearned Revenue		
Accounts Receivable		
Accounts Payable		
Owner's Capital		
Owner's Drawings		
Prepaid Rent		
Rent Expense		

AP-4A (❸ ❹)

Kick-off Sports Training helps train children in various sporting activities. During May 2016, the following transactions took place.

May 3	Received maintenance bill for $500 which will be paid next month.
May 3	Received $2,750 cash for training services provided.
May 4	Borrowed $4,000 cash from the bank.
May 4	Received $220 from a customer who owed money on training services already provided.
May 10	Prepaid $1,200 cash for insurance for one year.
May 10	Paid telephone expenses of $150 for the month with cash.
May 11	Paid $700 cash to reduce the amount owed to a supplier.
May 15	Paid $25 interest on the bank loan.

Required

Prepare the journal entries for the above transactions.

JOURNAL				Page 1
Date	Account Title and Explanation	PR	Debit	Credit

JOURNAL				Page 1
Date	**Account Title and Explanation**	**PR**	**Debit**	**Credit**

AP-5A (❸ ❹)

Rejuvenation Spa is a sole proprietorship owned by Claire Sawyer. The company provides a relaxing retreat for people wishing to relax and unwind. During the month of July 2016, the following transactions took place.

July 3	Provided services to a customer on account worth $3,600.
July 4	Borrowed $2,000 cash from the bank.
July 6	Provided services to a customer and received cash of $2,400.
July 10	Received the telephone bill for $250 which will be paid later.
July 11	Paid $600 cash to reduce the amount owed to a supplier.
July 15	Collected $1,800 cash from customers owing on account.
July 20	Paid the telephone bill from July 10.
July 21	Paid a portion of bank loan principal with $1,500 cash.
July 31	Paid salaries for the month with $1,600 cash.
July 31	Purchased equipment for $1,900 which will be paid later.

Required

Prepare the journal entries for the above transactions.

JOURNAL				Page 1
Date	Account Title and Explanation	PR	Debit	Credit

AP-6A (❸ ❹)

Noel Dy opened a bed and breakfast. The following transactions occurred during the month of March 2016.

Mar 1	Noel Dy invested $10,000 cash and $8,000 worth of furniture in the business.
Mar 3	Paid $1,000 cash to repair plumbing.
Mar 5	Purchased $1,200 worth of towels using cash.
Mar 7	Received $2,000 cash for room sales to MJ Gonzales.
Mar 8	Purchased additional towels from Adrian Cruz worth $1,000 on account.
Mar 15	Paid half of the amount due to Adrian Cruz with cash.
Mar 18	Paid $200 cash to local publication for advertising.
Mar 19	Paid $1,000 of salaries with cash.
Mar 20	Noel Dy withdrew $1,500 cash for personal use.
Mar 29	Bought $1,000 worth of chairs and tables for the bed and breakfast on account.
Mar 31	Noel Dy personally invested additional furniture worth $5,000 for business use.
Mar 31	Received $3,000 cash from various customers for room sales.

Required

Prepare journal entries for the above transactions.

JOURNAL				Page 1
Date	Account Title and Explanation	PR	Debit	Credit

JOURNAL				Page 1
Date	**Account Title and Explanation**	**PR**	**Debit**	**Credit**

AP-7A (❸❹❺❻)

Thomas Research provides market research services to hospitality companies. The company is owned and operated by Thomas Edwards. The closing balances at the end of March 2016 and the chart of accounts are shown below.

Thomas Research
Balance Sheet
As at March 31, 2016

Assets		**Liabilities**	
Cash	$22,000	Accounts Payable	$10,500
Accounts Receivable	9,000	Unearned Revenue	4,500
Equipment	8,000	Bank Loan	6,000
		Total Liabilities	21,000
		Owner's Equity	
		Edwards, Capital	18,000
Total Assets	$39,000	**Total Liabilities & Owner's Equity**	$39,000

Account Description	Account #
ASSETS	
Cash	101
Accounts Receivable	105
Prepaid Insurance	110
Equipment	120
LIABILITIES	
Accounts Payable	200
Unearned Revenue	210
Bank Loan	215
OWNER'S EQUITY	
Edwards, Capital	300
Edwards, Drawings	310

Account Description	Account #
REVENUE	
Service Revenue	400
EXPENSES	
Insurance Expense	515
Interest Expense	520
Rent Expense	540
Salaries Expense	545
Telephone Expense	550
Travel Expense	555

During the month of April, Thomas Research had the following transactions.

Apr 1	Purchased office equipment on account worth $7,000.
Apr 2	Received $25,000 cash for services provided.
Apr 3	Paid $1,000 cash for April's rent.
Apr 4	Prepaid $1,200 for insurance for one year.
Apr 10	Paid $200 cash to reduce the balance of accounts payable.
Apr 14	Paid $8,000 cash for employee's salaries.
Apr 22	Received telephone bill for $250 which will be paid next month.
Apr 24	Recorded travel expenses for $8,000 to be paid next month.
Apr 30	Paid $4,550 to bank for the bank loan principal and interest. Interest was $50 and remainder was principal.

Required

a) Prepare the journal entries for the month of April.
b) Post the journal entries to the ledger accounts.
c) Prepare a trial balance at the end of April.

JOURNAL				Page 1
Date	**Account Title and Explanation**	**PR**	**Debit**	**Credit**

JOURNAL				Page 1
Date	Account Title and Explanation	PR	Debit	Credit

Account: Cash					GL No:	
Date	Description	PR	DR	CR	Balance	

Account:					GL No:	
Date	Description	PR	DR	CR	Balance	

Account:					**GL No:**	
Date	**Description**	**PR**	**DR**	**CR**	**Balance**	

Account:					**GL No:**	
Date	**Description**	**PR**	**DR**	**CR**	**Balance**	

Account:					**GL No:**	
Date	**Description**	**PR**	**DR**	**CR**	**Balance**	

Account:					**GL No:**	
Date	**Description**	**PR**	**DR**	**CR**	**Balance**	

Account:					GL No:	
Date	Description	PR	DR	CR	Balance	

Account:					GL No:	
Date	Description	PR	DR	CR	Balance	

Account:					GL No:	
Date	Description	PR	DR	CR	Balance	

Account:					GL No:	
Date	Description	PR	DR	CR	Balance	

Account:					GL No:	
Date	Description	PR	DR	CR	Balance	

Account:					GL No:	
Date	Description	PR	DR	CR	Balance	

Account:					GL No:	
Date	Description	PR	DR	CR	Balance	

Account:					GL No:	
Date	Description	PR	DR	CR	Balance	

Account:					GL No:	
Date	**Description**	**PR**	**DR**	**CR**	**Balance**	

Account:					GL No:	
Date	**Description**	**PR**	**DR**	**CR**	**Balance**	

Account Titles	**DR**	**CR**

AP-8A (❸ ❹ ❺ ❻)

High Flying Biplane provides sightseeing tours in vintage biplanes. The company is owned by Sky Bridges. The closing balances at the end of May 2016 and the chart of accounts are shown below.

High Flying Biplane Balance Sheet As at May 31, 2016			
Assets		**Liabilities**	
Cash	$8,000	Accounts Payable	$8,200
Accounts Receivable	6,000	Unearned Revenue	3,200
Prepaid Insurance	1,200	Bank Loan	20,000
Equipment	60,000	**Total Liabilities**	31,400
		Owner's Equity	
		Bridges, Capital	43,800
Total Assets	$75,200	**Total Liabilities & Owner's Equity**	$75,200

Account Description	Account #
ASSETS	
Cash	101
Accounts Receivable	105
Prepaid Insurance	110
Equipment	120
LIABILITIES	
Accounts Payable	200
Interest Payable	205
Unearned Revenue	210
Bank Loan	215
OWNER'S EQUITY	
Bridges, Capital	300
Bridges, Drawings	310

Account Description	Account #
REVENUE	
Service Revenue	400
EXPENSES	
Advertising Expense	500
Insurance Expense	515
Interest Expense	520
Telephone Expense	550

During the month of June, High Flying Biplane had the following transactions.

Jun 1	The owner invested $5,000 cash into the business.
Jun 2	Received $1,500 cash for tours that will be provided in August.
Jun 3	Received an advertising bill for $400 which will be paid next month.
Jun 4	Paid the telephone bill with $200 cash.
Jun 10	Provided tours worth $2,400 to a customer who will pay next month.
Jun 14	Purchased equipment with $4,000 cash.
Jun 20	Received payments totalling $1,600 from customers paying their accounts.
Jun 22	Paid $900 towards accounts payable.
Jun 24	Paid $1,000 towards the bank loan principal.
Jun 30	The owner withdrew $1,200 cash for personal use.

Required

a) Prepare the journal entries for the month of June.
b) Post the journal entries to the ledger accounts.
c) Prepare a trial balance at the end of June.

JOURNAL				Page 1
Date	Account Title and Explanation	PR	Debit	Credit

Account: Cash					GL No:	
Date	Description	PR	DR	CR	Balance	

Account:					GL No:	
Date	Description	PR	DR	CR	Balance	

Account:					GL No:	
Date	Description	PR	DR	CR	Balance	

Account:					GL No:	
Date	Description	PR	DR	CR	Balance	

Account:					GL No:	
Date	Description	PR	DR	CR	Balance	

Account:				GL No:		
Date	Description	PR	DR	CR	Balance	

Account:				GL No:		
Date	Description	PR	DR	CR	Balance	

Account:				GL No:		
Date	Description	PR	DR	CR	Balance	

Account:				GL No:		
Date	Description	PR	DR	CR	Balance	

Account:				GL No:		
Date	Description	PR	DR	CR	Balance	

Account:					GL No:	
Date	Description	PR	DR	CR	Balance	

Account:					GL No:	
Date	Description	PR	DR	CR	Balance	

Account:					GL No:	
Date	Description	PR	DR	CR	Balance	

Account:					GL No:	
Date	Description	PR	DR	CR	Balance	

Account:					GL No:	
Date	Description	PR	DR	CR	Balance	

Account Titles	**DR**	**CR**

AP-9A (6)

Micro Tours, owned by Steven Upton, showed these accounts and their corresponding normal balances on May 31, 2016.

Account Titles	Balance
Upton, Capital	$23,500
Insurance Expense	900
Accounts Payable	15,500
Service Revenue	8,900
Equipment	34,500
Supplies Expense	3,000
Cash	6,400
Salaries Expense	4,000
Rent Expense	3,000
Upton, Drawings	3,000
Utilities Expense	1,300
Bank Loan	10,200
Prepaid Insurance	2,000

Required

Prepare Micro Tours' trial balance at May 31, 2016.

Account Titles	**DR**	**CR**

AP-10A (6)

Home Circus is owned by Laura Roberts and provides acrobatic entertainment at children's parties and other events. Its complete general ledger for March 2016 is shown below.

Account:	**Cash**				**GL No:**	**101**
Date	**Description**	**PR**	**DR**	**CR**	**Balance**	
Mar 1	Opening Balance				7,800	DR
Mar 1		J1		1,800	6,000	DR
Mar 2		J1	2,900		8,900	DR
Mar 3		J1		1,440	7,460	DR
Mar 10		J1		10	7,450	DR
Mar 10		J1		780	6,670	DR
Mar 20		J1	2,600		9,270	DR
Mar 22		J1	800		10,070	DR
Mar 24		J1		710	9,360	DR
Mar 31		J1		2,000	7,360	DR

Account:	Accounts Receivable				GL No:	105
Date	Description	PR	DR	CR	Balance	
Mar 1	Opening Balance				2,460	DR
Mar 22		J1		800	1,660	DR

Account:	Prepaid Insurance				GL No:	110
Date	Description	PR	DR	CR	Balance	
Mar 1	Opening Balance				0	DR
Mar 1		J1	1,800		1,800	DR

Account:	Office Supplies				GL No:	115
Date	Description	PR	DR	CR	Balance	
Mar 1	Opening Balance				640	DR
Mar 4		J1	250		890	DR

Account:	Equipment				GL No:	120
Date	Description	PR	DR	CR	Balance	
Mar 1	Opening Balance				10,500	DR
Mar 20		J1		2,600	7,900	DR

Account:	Accounts Payable				GL No:	200
Date	Description	PR	DR	CR	Balance	
Mar 1	Opening Balance				2,900	CR
Mar 4		J1		250	3,150	CR
Mar 24		J1	710		2,440	CR

Account:	Unearned Revenue				GL No:	210
Date	Description	PR	DR	CR	Balance	
Mar 1	Opening Balance				1,800	CR

Account:	Bank Loan				GL No:	215
Date	Description	PR	DR	CR	Balance	
Mar 1	Opening Balance				5,100	CR
Mar 10		J1	780		4,320	CR

Account:	Roberts, Capital				GL No:	300
Date	Description	PR	DR	CR	Balance	
Mar 1	Opening Balance				11,600	CR

Account:	Roberts, Drawing				GL No:	310
Date	Description	PR	DR	CR	Balance	
Mar 31		J1	2,000		2,000	DR

Account:	Service Revenue				GL No:	400
Date	Description	PR	DR	CR	Balance	
Mar 2		J1		2,900	2,900	CR

Account:	Office Supplies Expense				GL No:	520
Date	Description	PR	DR	CR	Balance	
Mar 10		J1	10		10	DR

Account:	Rent Expense				GL No:	540
Date	Description	PR	DR	CR	Balance	
Mar 3		J1	1,440		1,440	DR

Required

Prepare a trial balance. Place the accounts in the order shown in the general ledger.

Account Titles	DR	CR

AP-11A (❶ ❻)

A part-time bookkeeper for Wombat Eco-Adventure Tours has created the trial balance at the end of the year and cannot get it to balance.

Wombat Eco-Adventure Tours Trial Balance December 31, 2016		
Account Titles	**DR**	**CR**
Accounts Payable	$3,150	
Accounts Receivable	2,350	
Advertising Expense		$2,100
Bank Loan		5,200
Sharpe, Capital		6,170
Cash	6,200	
Interest Expense	560	
Maintenance Expense	240	
Office Supplies		1,600
Sharpe, Drawings		2,300
Prepaid Insurance	1,200	
Equipment	13,500	
Rent Expense	6,200	
Salaries Expense	5,300	
Service Revenue		25,800
Telephone Expense	450	
Unearned Revenue	1,680	
Total	$40,830	$43,170

All the entries have been journalized and posted to the general ledger properly, and all the accounts should have normal balances.

Required

Recreate the trial balance for Wombat Eco-Adventure Tours so that the accounts are listed in the order they would typically appear in a chart of accounts, and ensure that debits equal credits.

Account Titles	DR	CR

AP-12A (❸ ❹)

Greg Carlin is the owner of Carlin Consulting. During the month of April 2016 he had the following transactions.

Apr 1	Greg invested $5,000 cash and equipment valued at $3,000 into the business.
Apr 3	Provided consulting services to a customer. The customer paid $1,000 now and will pay $1,500 later.
Apr 6	Received a loan from the bank for $6,000.
Apr 8	Paid $1,300 for utilities for the month.
Apr 17	Purchased equipment with $4,000 cash.
Apr 20	Paid employee salaries with $2,100 cash.
Apr 22	Provided consulting services to a customer on account for $1,600.
Apr 28	Received the balance owing from the customer on April 3.

Required

Record the transactions in the journal.

JOURNAL				Page 1
Date	Account Title and Explanation	PR	Debit	Credit

Application Questions Group B

AP-1B (❶ ❸)

Pretty Paws is owned by Shelly Fisher and provides pet grooming services. During April 2016, Pretty Paws had the following transactions.

Apr 1 The owner invested $5,800 cash into the business.
Apr 4 Provided dog grooming services for a customer for $740. The customer will pay later.
Apr 6 Paid $600 cash for rent for the month.
Apr 8 Received a $370 telephone bill which will be paid later.
Apr 15 Paid $300 towards the bank loan principal.
Apr 19 Received cash from a customer who owed $840.
Apr 27 Paid the telephone bill received earlier.

Required

Complete the table to analyze each transaction.

	Account Name	Category	Increase or Decrease	Debit or Credit
Apr 1				
Apr 4				
Apr 6				
Apr 8				
Apr 15				
Apr 19				
Apr 27				

AP-2B (❶ ❸)

Bendari Tutoring Services had the following transactions for the month of November 2016.

Nov 1 Purchased supplies for $100 on account.
Nov 4 Received $4,200 cash from clients as payment for tutoring.
Nov 9 Received a telephone bill in the mail for $150.
Nov 16 Paid an employee's salary of $3,500 in cash.
Nov 25 Collected $500 from clients who owed money for previous services.

Required

Complete the table to analyze each transaction.

	Account Name	Category	Increase or Decrease	Debit or Credit
Nov 1				
Nov 4				
Nov 9				
Nov 16				
Nov 25				

AP-3B (❶)

For the accounts listed below, determine if the normal balance is a debit or a credit. Also, indicate if a debit or a credit will be needed to decrease the account balance.

	Account Title	Normal Balance	Decrease
1	Cash		
2	Accounts Receivable		
3	Accounts Payable		
4	Loan Payable		
5	Owner's Capital		
6	Service Revenue		
7	Insurance Expense		
8	Prepaid Insurance		
9	Equipment		
10	Unearned Revenue		
11	Owner's Drawings		
12	Salaries Expense		
13	Office Supplies		

AP-4B (❸ ❹)

Exhale Yoga provides a relaxing yoga retreat for people wishing to relax and unwind. During the month of July 2016, the following transactions took place.

Jul 3	Provided services to a customer and received $3,100 cash.
Jul 4	Borrowed $2,500 from the bank.
Jul 6	Provided services worth $2,800 to a customer on account.
Jul 10	Received the utilities bill for $240, which will be paid later.
Jul 11	Paid $690 cash to reduce the balance of accounts payable.
Jul 15	Collected $1,900 cash from customers owing on account.
Jul 20	Paid $2,600 towards the bank loan principal.
Jul 21	Paid the amount owing from July 10.
Jul 27	Paid salaries of $1,700 for the month with cash.
Jul 31	Purchased equipment worth $3,100 which will be paid later.

Required

Prepare the journal entries for the above transactions.

JOURNAL				**Page 1**
Date	**Account Title and Explanation**	**PR**	**Debit**	**Credit**

JOURNAL				Page 1
Date	Account Title and Explanation	PR	Debit	Credit

AP-5B (❸ ❹)

Caretree Arborist Services provides tree pruning and removal services to homeowners, golf courses and municipalities. During the month of February 2016, Caretree Arborist Services had the following transactions.

Feb 1	Purchased equipment worth $8,200, which will be paid later.
Feb 2	Provided services worth $20,200 to a customer on account.
Feb 3	Paid $1,900 cash for February's utilities.
Feb 4	Paid $1,600 for four months of insurance coverage.
Feb 10	Paid $2,000 cash to reduce the balance of accounts payable.
Feb 14	Paid $6,600 cash for monthly maintenance contract.
Feb 22	Billed for $5,800 in travel expenses to be paid next month.
Feb 24	Received an advertising bill for $400 which will be paid next month.
Feb 28	Paid $2,730 to the bank to reduce the bank loan principal. Interest was $30 and the remainder was principal.

Required

Prepare the journal entries for the above transactions.

JOURNAL				**Page 1**
Date	**Account Title and Explanation**	**PR**	**Debit**	**Credit**

AP-6B (❸ ④)

Cherry Consulting Firm is owned by Ron Cherry and offers consulting services for small businesses. During June 2016, the following transactions occurred.

Jun 2	Received a deposit of $3,000 from a customer for services to be provided in the future.
Jun 3	Paid a $495 utility bill that was received and recorded last month.
Jun 8	Charged $1,400 in travel costs to a credit card.
Jun 17	Paid $1,000 cash to reduce the bank loan. Of that amount, $75 is interest and the remainder is principal.
Jun 19	Ron withdrew $2,100 cash from the business for personal use.
Jun 28	Paid $4,900 for salaries for the month.

Required

Prepare the journal entries for the above transactions.

JOURNAL				Page 1
Date	**Account Title and Explanation**	**PR**	**Debit**	**Credit**

AP-7B (❸ ❹ ❺ ❻)

Crystal Clear provides professional pool cleaning services. The company is a sole proprietorship owned by Crystal Lowe. The closing balances at the end of August 2016 and the chart of accounts are shown below.

Crystal Clear Balance Sheet As at August 31, 2016			
Assets		**Liabilities**	
Cash	$7,200	Accounts Payable	$3,400
Accounts Receivable	2,300	Unearned Revenue	1,400
Office Supplies	850	Bank Loan	5,600
Equipment	11,500	**Total Liabilities**	10,400
		Owner's Equity	
		Lowe, Capital	11,450
Total Assets	$21,850	**Total Liabilities & Owner's Equity**	$21,850

Account Description	Account #
ASSETS	
Cash	101
Accounts Receivable	105
Prepaid Insurance	110
Office Supplies	115
Equipment	120
LIABILITIES	
Accounts Payable	200
Unearned Revenue	210
Bank Loan	215
OWNER'S EQUITY	
Lowe, Capital	300
Lowe, Drawings	310

Account Description	Account #
REVENUE	
Service Revenue	400
EXPENSES	
Insurance Expense	515
Interest Expense	520
Office Supplies Expense	530
Rent Expense	540

During the month of September, Crystal Clear had the following transactions.

Sep 1	Paid $1,800 cash in advance for a one-year insurance policy.
Sep 2	Received $1,900 cash for services provided.
Sep 3	Paid $1,350 cash for September's rent.
Sep 4	Purchased office supplies on account worth $250.
Sep 10	Paid $960 towards the bank loan principal and $40 of interest on the loan.
Sep 20	Received $2,200 cash from a customer booking a pool cleaning in advance.
Sep 22	Collected $850 from a customer paying their account.
Sep 24	Paid $600 towards accounts payable.
Sep 30	The owner withdrew $1,600 cash for personal use.

Required

a) Prepare the journal entries for the month of September.
b) Post the journal entries to the ledger accounts.
c) Prepare a trial balance at the end of September.

JOURNAL				Page 1
Date	Account Title and Explanation	PR	Debit	Credit

Account: Cash **GL No:**

Date	Description	PR	DR	CR	Balance	

Account: **GL No:**

Date	Description	PR	DR	CR	Balance	

Account: **GL No:**

Date	Description	PR	DR	CR	Balance	

Account: **GL No:**

Date	Description	PR	DR	CR	Balance	

Account: **GL No:**

Date	Description	PR	DR	CR	Balance	

Account:					GL No:	
Date	Description	PR	DR	CR	Balance	

Account:					GL No:	
Date	Description	PR	DR	CR	Balance	

Account:					GL No:	
Date	Description	PR	DR	CR	Balance	

Account:					GL No:	
Date	Description	PR	DR	CR	Balance	

Account:					GL No:	
Date	Description	PR	DR	CR	Balance	

Account:					GL No:	
Date	Description	PR	DR	CR	Balance	

Account:					GL No:	
Date	Description	PR	DR	CR	Balance	

Account:					GL No:	
Date	Description	PR	DR	CR	Balance	

Account:					GL No:	
Date	Description	PR	DR	CR	Balance	

Account:					GL No:	
Date	Description	PR	DR	CR	Balance	

Account Titles	**DR**	**CR**

AP-8B (❸ ❹ ❺ ❻)

Sokatoa, a carpet cleaning business owned by Susan Wethers, had the following transactions for the month of July 2016.

Jul 1	Purchased a new machine with $12,000 cash.
Jul 5	Provided services worth $10,000 to clients who will pay later.
Jul 12	Susan withdrew $5,000 cash from the business.
Jul 19	Received a maintenance bill for $1,100 which will be paid later.
Jul 31	Got a loan from the bank for $25,000.

Required

Journalize the transactions, post them to the general ledger, and prepare a trial balance.

JOURNAL				Page 1
Date	Account Title and Explanation	PR	Debit	Credit

Account:	Cash				GL No:	101
Date: 2016	Description	PR	DR	CR	Balance (DR or CR)	
	Opening Balance				31,800	DR

Account:	Accounts Receivable				GL No:	105
Date: 2016	Description	PR	DR	CR	Balance (DR or CR)	
	Opening Balance				5,000	DR

Account:	Machine				GL No:	120
Date: 2016	Description	PR	DR	CR	Balance (DR or CR)	
	Opening Balance				6,000	DR

Account:	Accounts Payable				GL No:	200
Date: 2016	Description	PR	DR	CR	Balance (DR or CR)	
	Opening Balance				3,500	CR

Account:	Bank Loan				GL No:	215
Date: 2016	Description	PR	DR	CR	Balance (DR or CR)	
	Opening Balance				0	CR

Account:	Wethers, Capital				GL No:	300
Date: 2016	Description	PR	DR	CR	Balance (DR or CR)	
	Opening Balance				39,300	CR

Account:	Wethers, Drawings				GL No:	310
Date: 2016	Description	PR	DR	CR	Balance (DR or CR)	

Account:	Sales Revenue				GL No:	400
Date: 2016	Description	PR	DR	CR	Balance (DR or CR)	

Account:	Maintenance Expense				GL No:	520
Date: 2016	Description	PR	DR	CR	Balance (DR or CR)	

Account:	Salaries Expense				GL No:	540
Date: 2016	Description	PR	DR	CR	Balance (DR or CR)	

Account Titles	DR	CR

Analysis

Explain how the general ledger is similar to the T-accounts used in earlier chapters.

____

____

____

____

AP-9B (❶ ❻)

The following are the accounts of DRAM Company and their corresponding normal balances on October 31, 2016.

Account	Balance
David, Capital	$20,400
Accounts Payable	13,200
Insurance Expense	1,000
Service Revenue	6,800
Equipment	30,500
Supplies Expense	2,900
Cash	5,700
Salaries Expense	4,100
David, Drawings	3,100
Rent Expense	2,200
Telephone Expense	1,200
Bank Loan	11,700
Prepaid Rent	1,400

Required

Prepare DRAM Company's trial balance for the month ended October 31, 2016.

Account Titles	**DR**	**CR**

AP-10B (❻)

The following account balances were taken from Macro Company's general ledger on February 29, 2016.

Account	Balance
Chalmers, Capital	$10,050
Accounts Payable	13,000
Prepaid Expenses	5,000
Interest Payable	825
Vehicle	32,000
Computer Equipment	19,000
Salary Expense	31,000
Unearned Revenue	8,000
Depreciation Expense	1,700
Rent Expense	2,400
Cash	15,275
Service Revenue	74,500

Required

Prepare Macro Company's trial balance.

Account Titles	**DR**	**CR**

Analysis

The accountant at Macro Company was worried that he may have recorded some entries incorrectly in the journal, but upon seeing that the trial balance is in balance, realized that he must have done everything correctly. Is this true or false? Explain.

____

____

____

____

AP-11B (❶)

Indicate whether increases and decreases in the following groups of accounts correspond to debits or credits.

	Increase	**Decrease**
Liabilities		
Owner's Equity		
Expenses		
Owner's Drawings		
Revenues		
Assets		

Analysis

What is a normal balance?

____

____

____

AP-12B (❸ ❹)

Helen Long owns and operates Long Landscaping which provides landscaping and gardening services. During the month of August 2016, she had the following transactions.

Aug 1	Provided services to a customer who paid $800 cash.
Aug 3	Paid $1,000 to the bank to repay a bank loan. Of that amount, $100 was interest.
Aug 6	Received a maintenance bill for $500 which will be paid later.
Aug 8	Paid $1,600 for a one-year insurance policy.
Aug 17	Paid $2,200 for rent for the month.
Aug 20	Provided services to a customer for $1,300 and the customer will pay later.
Aug 22	Paid the maintenance bill received on August 6.
Aug 28	Received payment from the customer from August 20.

Required

Record the transactions in the journal.

JOURNAL				Page 1
Date	Account Title and Explanation	PR	Debit	Credit

JOURNAL				Page 1
Date	**Account Title and Explanation**	**PR**	**Debit**	**Credit**

Notes

Chapter 5

THE ACCOUNTING CYCLE: ADJUSTMENTS

LEARNING OUTCOMES

❶ Describe the purpose of adjustments

❷ Prepare adjusting entries for accrued revenue

❸ Prepare adjusting entries for accrued expenses

❹ Prepare adjusting entries for unearned revenue

❺ Prepare adjusting entries for prepaid expenses

❻ Prepare adjusting entries for depreciation

❼ Prepare an adjusted trial balance

Appendix

❽ Prepare correcting entries

AMEENGAGE *Access **ameengage.com** for integrated resources including tutorials, practice exercises, the digital textbook and more.*

Assessment Questions

AS-1 (❼)

What is the purpose of a worksheet?

____

____

AS-2 (❶)

Why must adjustments be made at the end of the accounting period?

____

____

AS-3 (❹)

When making an adjustment to record unearned revenue that is now earned, which accounts are used and how are they affected?

____

____

____

____

AS-4 (❻)

When making an adjustment to record depreciation on equipment, which accounts are used and how are they affected?

AS-5 (❻)

What is the purpose of a contra account?

AS-6 (❻)

True or False: All assets that are part of property, plant and equipment depreciate.

AS-7 (❺)

When making an adjustment to record the used portion of prepaid insurance, which accounts are used and how are they affected?

AS-8 (❸)

When making an adjustment to record accrued interest on a bank loan, which accounts are used and how are they affected?

AS-9 (❼)

What is an adjusted trial balance?

____

____

AS-10 (❻)

How does accumulated depreciation affect the value of property, plant and equipment?

____

____

AS-11 (❶)

What is an accounting period?

____

____

AS-12 (❶)

What does accrual-based accounting state regarding revenue and expenses?

____

____

____

AS-13 (❷ ❸ ❹ ❺ ❻)

Provide five examples of adjustments.

____

____

____

____

____

____

AS-14 (❸)

Define accrued expenses.

AS-15 (❸)

What is the entry to recognize accrued interest expense?

Application Questions Group A

AP-1A (❹ ❺ ❻ ❼)

Swordfish Aquarium is owned by Mark Kulak and operates a public aquarium in one of the metropolitan areas in Canada. At the end of April 2016, Swordfish had the following adjustments.

Apr 30	A count of office supplies showed that there was $550 remaining in the office.
Apr 30	The balance of prepaid insurance is for a 12-month policy, one month of insurance has been used.
Apr 30	During April, Swordfish Aquarium earned $900 of unearned revenue.
Apr 30	An aquarium equipment was purchased on April 1, 2016 and have an expected useful life of five years, after which they will have no residual value. Record the depreciation for April.

Required

Using the following trial balance, complete the adjustments and the adjusted trial balance in the worksheet.

Swordfish Aquarium
Worksheet
April 30, 2016

	Unadjusted Trial Balance		Adjustments		Adjusted Trial Balance	
Account Titles	**DR**	**CR**	**DR**	**CR**	**DR**	**CR**
Cash	$4,200				4200	
Accounts Receivable	2,300				2300	
Prepaid Insurance	1,800			150	1650	
Office Supplies	800			250	550	
Equipment	9,600				9600	
Accumulated Depreciation—Equipment		$0		160		160
Accounts Payable		1,640				1640
Unearned Revenue		1,950	900			1050
Bank Loan		3,200				3200
Kulak, Capital		10,235				10,235
Kulak, Drawings	1,500				1500	
Service Revenue		4,750		900		5650
Depreciation Expense	0		160		160	
Insurance Expense	0		150		150	
Office Supplies Expense	0		250		250	
Rent Expense	1,300				1300	
Telephone Expense	275				275	
Total	$21,775	$21,775	1460	1460	21,935	21,935

AP-2A (❸ ❹ ❺ ❻ ❼)

Chirp Fitness operates a chain of health clubs across Canada. At the end of November 2016, the company had the following adjustments.

Nov 30	Interest on the bank loan is set at 10%. One month of interest has accrued.
Nov 30	The balance of the prepaid insurance is for the remaining 10 months of the insurance policy. One month of insurance has been used.
Nov 30	An exercise equipment was purchased on September 1, 2016 and will have a useful life of 7 years, after which it will have no residual value. Depreciation is recorded every month. Record depreciation for November.
Nov 30	Membership revenue of $650 that was previously unearned has become earned.
Nov 30	Office supplies used during the month totalled $400.

Required

Using the following trial balance, complete the adjustments and the adjusted trial balance in the worksheet.

Chirp Fitness Worksheet November 30, 2016						
	Unadjusted Trial Balance		Adjustments		Adjusted Trial Balance	
Account Titles	**DR**	**CR**	**DR**	**CR**	**DR**	**CR**
Cash	$6,250					
Accounts Receivable	3,440					
Prepaid Insurance	2,200					
Office Supplies	1,140					
Equipment	15,120					
Accumulated Depreciation—Equipment		$360				
Accounts Payable		2,260				
Interest Payable		0				
Unearned Revenue		1,240				
Bank Loan		4,800				
Earring, Capital		12,640				
Earring, Drawings	2,100					
Service Revenue		12,500				
Depreciation Expense	0					
Insurance Expense	0					
Interest Expense	0					
Office Supplies Expense	0					
Rent Expense	1,650					
Salaries Expense	1,900					
Total	$33,800	$33,800				

AP-3A (❷ ❸ ❺ ❻)

Mr. Allan Poe operates an advertising business called A Advertising. He had the following adjustments for the month of December 2016.

Dec 31	Recognized $1,250 rent expense used for the month.
Dec 31	An annual magazine subscription was prepaid on December 1, 2016 for $600. By December 31, one issue had been received.
Dec 31	Depreciation on equipment for the month is $400.
Dec 31	Salaries for employees have accrued by $1,300 by the end of the month.
Dec 31	A 30-day contract was started on December 16. The customer will pay $5,000 at the end of the contract in January. Accrue the revenue earned by the end of December.

Required

Prepare the journal entries for the adjustments.

JOURNAL				**Page 1**
Date	**Account Titles and Explanation**	**PR**	**Debit**	**Credit**

AP-4A (❸ ❹ ❺ ❻)

MJ Event Planning Services is in its second year of operations. At the end of April 2016, it had the following adjustments. Adjustments have not been made since December 31, 2015.

Apr 30	A one-year insurance policy was purchased on January 1, 2016 for $3,600. Record the insurance used.
Apr 30	Depreciation on equipment is $200 per month.
Apr 30	A count of office supplies showed that $650 had been used.
Apr 30	Accrued interest on a bank loan was $30.
Apr 30	Outstanding work for a client worth $800 was completed during the month. The client had paid for the work last year.

Required

Prepare the journal entries for the adjustments.

JOURNAL				Page 1
Date	**Account Titles and Explanation**	**PR**	**Debit**	**Credit**

AP-5A (❹ ❺ ❻ ❼)

Sigmund Travel Services has completed all its journal entries for the month of April 2016 and posted them to the general ledger. Based on the ledger balances, an unadjusted trial balance has been prepared.

Sigmund Travel Services Unadjusted Trial Balance April 30, 2016		
Account Titles	**DR**	**CR**
Cash	$32,050	
Accounts Receivable	9,000	
Prepaid Insurance	1,200	
Equipment	15,000	
Accounts Payable		$25,550
Unearned Revenue		4,500
Bank Loan		1,500
Sigmund, Capital		18,000
Service Revenue		25,000
Interest Expense	50	
Rent Expense	1,000	
Salaries Expense	8,000	
Telephone Expense	250	
Travel Expense	8,000	
Total	$74,550	$74,550

The following adjustments must be made at the end of April.

Apr 30 The balance of prepaid insurance represents a 12-month policy. One month has been used.

Apr 30 Depreciation of equipment for the month is $120.

Apr 30 Sigmund Travel Services has earned $1,300 that was previously unearned.

Required

a) Fill in the unadjusted trial balance on the worksheet and complete the rest of the worksheet.

b) Create the journal entries for the adjustments from the worksheet.

Sigmund Travel Services Unadjusted Trial Balance April 30, 2016						
	Unadjusted Trial Balance		Adjustments		Adjusted Trial Balance	
Account Titles	DR	CR	DR	CR	DR	CR
Cash	32,050				32050	
Accounts Receivable	9000				9000.	
Prepaid Insurance	1,200			100.	1100	
Equipment	15,000				15000.	
Accounts Payable		25,550				25550
Unearned Revenue		4,500	1,300			3,200
Bank Loan		1,500				1,500
Sigmund, Capital.		18,000				18,000
Service Revenue		25,000		1,300		26,3000
Interest Expense	50				50	
Rent Exp.	1,000				1000.	
Salaries Exp	8,000				8000	
Telephone Exp.	250				250	
Travel Exp	8,000				8000	
Total.	74,550	74,550				
Insurance Exp.			100		100	
Depreciation Equip			120		120.	
Accumu Depreciation.				120.		120.
			1520	1,520.	74670	74670

JOURNAL				Page 2
Date	Account Titles and Explanation	PR	Debit	Credit
Apr 30.	Insurance Expense.		100	
	Prepaid Insurance.			100.
	updated Insurance			
Apr 30.	Depreciation Expense.		120	
	Accumulated Dep.			120
	updated depriciation.			
Apr 30	Unearned Fees.		1300	
	Service Revenue.			1300
	updated Revenue earned			

AP-6A (❸ ❹ ❺ ❻ ❼)

High Flying Biplane, owned by Sky Bridges, has completed all its journal entries for the month of June 2016 and posted them to the general ledger. Based on the ledger balances, an unadjusted trial balance has been prepared.

High Flying Biplane Unadjusted Trial Balance June 30, 2016		
Account Titles	**DR**	**CR**
Cash	$8,800	
Accounts Receivable	6,800	
Prepaid Insurance	1,200	
Equipment	64,000	
Accounts Payable		$7,700
Unearned Revenue		4,700
Bank Loan		19,000
Bridges, Capital		48,800
Bridges, Drawings	1,200	
Service Revenue		2,400
Advertising Expense	400	
Telephone Expense	200	
Total	$82,600	$82,600

The following adjustments must be made at the end of June.

Jun 30 One month of insurance worth $100 has been used.
Jun 30 Depreciation on the equipment was $450 this month.
Jun 30 Of the unearned revenue amount, $4,080 still remains unearned.
Jun 30 Interest accrued on the bank loan was $75.

Required

a) Fill in the unadjusted trial balance on the worksheet and complete the rest of the worksheet.

b) Create the journal entries for the adjustments from the worksheet.

	Unadjusted Trial Balance		Adjustments		Adjusted Trial Balance	
Account Titles	DR	CR	DR	CR	DR	CR

JOURNAL				Page 2
Date	Account Titles and Explanation	PR	Debit	Credit

AP-7A (❹❺❻❼)

Home Circus has completed all its journal entries for the month of September 2016 and posted them to the general ledger. Based on the ledger balances, an unadjusted trial balance has been prepared.

Home Circus Unadjusted Trial Balance September 30, 2016		
Account Titles	**DR**	**CR**
Cash	$5,800	
Accounts Receivable	1,450	
Prepaid Insurance	1,800	
Office Supplies	1,100	
Equipment	9,300	
Accounts Payable		$3,050
Unearned Revenue		1,400
Bank Loan		4,640
Roberts, Capital		11,450
Roberts, Drawings	1,600	
Service Revenue		1,900
Interest Expense	40	
Rent Expense	1,350	
Total	$22,440	$22,440

The following adjustments must be made at the end of September.

Sep 30 The amount of prepaid insurance is for 12 months. Once month has been used.
Sep 30 Depreciation for the month on equipment was $120.
Sep 30 Unearned revenue of $360 has now been earned.
Sep 30 A count of office supplies shows that $650 remains.

Required

a) Fill in the unadjusted trial balance on the worksheet and complete the rest of the worksheet.

b) Create the journal entries for the adjustments from the worksheet.

	Unadjusted Trial Balance		Adjustments		Adjusted Trial Balance	
Account Titles	DR	CR	DR	CR	DR	CR

JOURNAL				Page 2
Date	Account Titles and Explanation	PR	Debit	Credit

AP-8A (❸❹❺❻❼)

Zig Zag Gardening Services has the following adjustments to make at the end of September 2016, the end of its fiscal year.

Sep 30 Unearned revenue of $850 has now been earned.

Sep 30 A count of the office supplies shows that $430 worth still remains on hand.

Sep 30 Salaries accrued but not yet paid amount to $2,430.

Sep 30 Monthly depreciation on equipment was $600.

The chart of accounts is shown below.

Account Description	Account #
ASSETS	
Cash	101
Accounts Receivable	105
Office Supplies	110
Equipment	120
Accumulated Depreciation—Equipment	130
LIABILITIES	
Accounts Payable	200
Unearned Revenue	210
Salaries Payable	220

Account Description	Account #
OWNER'S EQUITY	
Rizzo, Capital	300
Rizzo, Drawings	310
REVENUE	
Service Revenue	400
EXPENSES	
Salaries Expense	530
Depreciation Expense	535
Supplies Expense	540

Required

a) Complete the six-column worksheet.

b) Journalize the adjustments.

c) Post the transactions to the general ledger accounts provided.

Zig Zag Gardening Services Worksheet September 30, 2016						
	Unadjusted Trial Balance		Adjustments		Adjusted Trial Balance	
Account Titles	**DR**	**CR**	**DR**	**CR**	**DR**	**CR**
Cash	$3,000					
Accounts Receivable	950					
Office Supplies	830					
Equipment	5,500					
Accumulated Depreciation—Equipment		$1,800				
Accounts Payable		1,250				
Unearned Revenue		1,700				
Rizzo, Capital		4,030				
Rizzo, Drawings	500					
Service Revenue		4,200				
Salaries Expense	2,200					
Total	$12,980	$12,980				

JOURNAL				Page 1
Date	**Account Title and Explanation**	**PR**	**Debit**	**Credit**

Account:	Office Supplies				GL No:	110
Date: 2016	Description	PR	DR	CR	Balance (DR or CR)	
	Opening Balance					

Account:	Accumulated Depreciation—Equipment				GL No:	130
Date: 2016	Description	PR	DR	CR	Balance (DR or CR)	
	Opening Balance					

Account:	Unearned Revenue				GL No:	210
Date: 2016	Description	PR	DR	CR	Balance (DR or CR)	
	Opening Balance					

Account:	Salaries Payable				GL No:	220
Date: 2016	Description	PR	DR	CR	Balance (DR or CR)	
	Opening Balance					

Account:	Service Revenue				GL No:	400
Date: 2016	Description	PR	DR	CR	Balance (DR or CR)	
	Opening Balance					

Account:	Salaries Expense				GL No:	530
Date: 2016	Description	PR	DR	CR	Balance (DR or CR)	
	Opening Balance					

Account:	Depreciation Expense				GL No:	535
Date: 2016	Description	PR	DR	CR	Balance (DR or CR)	
	Opening Balance					

Account:	Supplies Expense				GL No:	540
Date: 2016	Description	PR	DR	CR	Balance (DR or CR)	
	Opening Balance					

Analysis

What is the purpose of preparing a worksheet before journalizing and posting adjusting entries, and before preparing financial statements?

____

____

____

____

AP-9A (6)

On January 1, 2016, Precision Airline purchased a new piece of equipment for $100,000. The equipment is expected to last five years and will have no residual value. Precision Airline has a December 31 year end. Prepare the table below showing the yearly depreciation, accumulated depreciation and net book value of the equipment.

Year	Original Cost of Equipment	Depreciation Expense	Accumulated Depreciation	Net Book Value
2016				
2017				
2018				
2019				
2020				
Total				

AP-10A (6)

On March 1, 2016, Jefferson Travel Agency purchased new computers for $19,000. The computers are expected to last three years and have an estimated residual value of $1,000. Jefferson has a December 31 year end. Prepare the table below showing the yearly depreciation, accumulated depreciation and net book value of the computers.

Year	Original Cost of Computers	Depreciation Expense	Accumulated Depreciation	Net Book Value
2016				
2017				
2018				
2019				
Total				

AP-11A (8)

On June 23, 2016, the bookkeeper for Rejuvenation Spa discovered an error in the journal entries. On June 2, equipment was purchased on account for $9,000, however it was recorded in the journals and ledgers for $90,000. Prepare the entries to correct this error.

JOURNAL				Page 1
Date	Account Titles and Explanation	PR	Debit	Credit

AP-12A (8)

On November 22, 2016, the bookkeeper for Esteem Fitness discovered an error in the journal entries. On November 16, an entry was made for the cash purchase of office supplies for $550 that in error debited equipment. Prepare the entries to correct this error.

JOURNAL				Page 1
Date	Account Titles and Explanation	PR	Debit	Credit

Application Questions Group B

AP-1B (❹❺❻❼)

Decodely Zoo operates a public zoo in a suburban area in Canada. At the end of December 2016, it had four adjustments.

Dec 31	During December, Decodely Programming earned $830 of unearned revenue.
Dec 31	$1,250 of office supplies was used during the month.
Dec 31	The balance of prepaid insurance represents 11 months remaining on the policy. One month of insurance has been used.
Dec 31	Equipment depreciated $110 during December.

Required

Using the following trial balance, complete the adjustments and the adjusted trial balance in the worksheet.

Decodely Zoo Worksheet December 31, 2016						
	Unadjusted Trial Balance		Adjustments		Adjusted Trial Balance	
Account Titles	**DR**	**CR**	**DR**	**CR**	**DR**	**CR**
Cash	$4,000					
Accounts Receivable	2,620					
Prepaid Insurance	2,750					
Office Supplies	1,790					
Equipment	9,400					
Accumulated Depreciation—Equipment		$400				
Accounts Payable		1,900				
Unearned Revenue		4,500				
Bank Loan		3,410				
Singh, Capital		9,930				
Singh, Drawings	1,560					
Service Revenue		4,090				
Depreciation Expense	0					
Insurance Expense	0					
Office Supplies Expense	0					
Rent Expense	1,970					
Utilities Expense	140					
Total	$24,230	$24,230				

AP-2B (❸❺❻❼)

Have-A-Bash, owned by Finn Tymes, has completed all the entries for the month of November 2016, except the monthly adjusting entries. The following information is available to make the adjustments.

Nov 30 Annual depreciation on equipment totals $9,000.
Nov 30 Interest accrued on the bank loan is $500.
Nov 30 Office supplies on hand are valued at $2,300.
Nov 30 The annual insurance policy was purchased on December 1, 2015 for $21,900.

Required

Complete the six-column worksheet for Have-A-Bash.

Have-A-Bash Worksheet November 30, 2016						
	Unadjusted Trial Balance		Adjustments		Adjusted Trial Balance	
Account Titles	**DR**	**CR**	**DR**	**CR**	**DR**	**CR**
Cash	$52,250					
Accounts Receivable	24,800					
Office Supplies	10,400					
Prepaid Insurance	1,825					
Equipment	295,400					
Accumulated Depreciation—Equipment		$107,250				
Accounts Payable		31,500				
Bank Loan		140,000				
Tymes, Capital		96,750				
Tymes, Drawings	60,000					
Service Revenue		382,500				
Advertising Expense	100,000					
Salaries Expense	185,000					
Insurance Expense	20,075					
Depreciation Expense	8,250					
Total	$758,000	$758,000				

AP-3B (❸ ④ ⑤ ⑥)

Sprig Gardening Service provides seasonal gardening services. At the end of August 2016, the company must make the following adjustments.

Aug 31	Depreciation for equipment is $120.
Aug 31	Interest due on a bank loan is $50. It will be paid next month.
Aug 31	Accrued salary expense for an employee at the end of the month. The company owes the employee $450.
Aug 31	One month of prepaid insurance at $70 per month has been used.
Aug 31	A physical count of office supplies shows that $300 was used during August.
Aug 31	Sprig Gardening earned $670 that was previously unearned.

Required

Prepare the adjusting journal entries.

JOURNAL				**Page 1**
Date	**Account Titles and Explanation**	**PR**	**Debit**	**Credit**

AP-4B (❸❹❺❻)

Speak Yoga operates a chain of yoga studios across Canada. At the end of March 2016, it had the following account balances and adjustments. Adjustments have not been made since December 31, 2015.

Speak Up Trial Balance March 31, 2016		
Account Titles	**DR**	**CR**
Cash	$6,380	
Accounts Receivable	3,590	
Prepaid Insurance	999	
Office Supplies	1,120	
Equipment	15,170	
Accumulated Depreciation—Equipment		$400
Accounts Payable		2,120
Unearned Revenue		1,570
Bank Loan		4,930
Jones, Capital		12,659
Jones, Drawings	2,930	
Service Revenue		12,570
Rent Expense	1,920	
Salaries Expense	2,140	
Total	$34,249	$34,249

Mar 31 Accrued $43 interest on the bank loan.
Mar 31 The balance of the prepaid insurance is for the remaining nine months of the insurance policy.
Mar 31 Membership revenue of $942 that was previously unearned has become earned.
Mar 31 Depreciation on equipment is $250 per month.
Mar 31 Office supplies used during the first three months totalled $448.

Required

Complete the adjusting entries.

JOURNAL				Page 1
Date	**Account Titles and Explanation**	**PR**	**Debit**	**Credit**

AP-5B (❹❺❻❼)

Thomas Research provides market research services to hospitality companies. It has completed journal entries for the month of October and posted them to the general ledger. Based on the ledger balances, an unadjusted trial balance has been prepared.

The following adjustments must be made at the end of October.

Oct 31 One month of prepaid rent worth $720 has been used.
Oct 31 Depreciation on equipment for the month was $340.
Oct 31 Unearned revenue worth $1,330 has now been earned.

Required

a) Fill in the unadjusted trial balance on the worksheet and complete the rest of the worksheet.
b) Create the journal entries for the adjustments from the worksheet.

Thomas Research Worksheet October 31, 2016						
	Unadjusted Trial Balance		Adjustments		Adjusted Trial Balance	
Account Titles	**DR**	**CR**	**DR**	**CR**	**DR**	**CR**
Cash	$32,000					
Accounts Receivable	9,500					
Prepaid Rent	5,760					
Equipment	15,000					
Accumulated Depreciation—Equipment		$950				
Accounts Payable		27,800				
Unearned Revenue		5,800				
Bank Loan		1,960				
Thomas, Capital		9,330				
Service Revenue		30,000				
Depreciation Expense						
Insurance Expense	570					
Interest Expense	150					
Rent Expense	0					
Salaries Expense	6,400					
Supplies Expense	360					
Utilities Expense	6,100					
Total	$75,840	$75,840				

JOURNAL				Page 1
Date	**Account Titles and Explanation**	**PR**	**Debit**	**Credit**

AP-6B (❸ ❹ ❺ ❻ ❼)

Floating Speed Boat has completed its journal entries for the month of September and posted them to the general ledger. Based on the ledger balances, an unadjusted trial balance has been prepared.

The following adjustments must be made at the end of September.

Sep 30	Depreciation on equipment for the month is $390.
Sep 30	Prepaid insurance of $250 has been used up this month.
Sep 30	Interest of $150 has accrued on the bank loan.
Sep 30	Unearned revenue of $570 has now been earned.

Required

a) Complete the worksheet.

b) Create the journal entries for the adjustments from the worksheet.

Floating Speed Boat
Worksheet
September 30, 2016

	Unadjusted Trial Balance		Adjustments		Adjusted Trial Balance	
Account Titles	**DR**	**CR**	**DR**	**CR**	**DR**	**CR**
Cash	$8,800					
Accounts Receivable	7,900					
Prepaid Insurance	1,500					
Equipment	64,000					
Accumulated Depreciation—Equipment		$870				
Accounts Payable		9,900				
Interest Payable		0				
Unearned Revenue		6,500				
Bank Loan		15,500				
Fathom, Capital		49,000				
Fathom, Drawings	1,200					
Service Revenue		3,400				
Advertising Expense	430					
Depreciation Expense	0					
Insurance Expense	0					
Interest Expense	0					
Rent Expense	1,340					
Total	$85,170	$85,170				

JOURNAL				Page 1
Date	Account Titles and Explanation	PR	Debit	Credit

AP-7B (❸❹❺❻❼)

Jordan Land Designs provides landscaping for hotels and resorts. Jordan Land Designs has already completed the transactions for the month and posted them to the general ledger. The adjustments for December 2016 have not yet been prepared.

Dec 31	Provided services worth $1,500 to customer who had paid in advance.
Dec 31	One month of insurance of $1,000 was used.
Dec 31	Depreciation for the month was $500.
Dec 31	Salaries accrued at the end of December amounted to $3,370.

Required

a) Prepare the six-column worksheet.

b) Record the journal entries for the adjusting entries.

Jordan Land Designs Worksheet December 31, 2016						
	Unadjusted Trial Balance		Adjustments		Adjusted Trial Balance	
Account Titles	**DR**	**CR**	**DR**	**CR**	**DR**	**CR**
Cash	$3,250					
Accounts Receivable	2,750					
Prepaid Insurance	13,000					
Equipment	285,000					
Accumulated Depreciation—Equipment		$45,000				
Accounts Payable		5,500				
Salaries Payable		0				
Unearned Revenue		3,600				
Bank Loan		191,680				
Jordan, Capital		46,200				
Jordan, Drawings	13,500					
Service Revenue		78,000				
Maintenance Expense	5,200					
Depreciation Expense	4,000					
Interest Expense	1,280					
Insurance Expense	11,000					
Salaries Expense	31,000					
Total	$369,980	$369,980				

JOURNAL				Page 2
Date	**Account Titles and Explanation**	**PR**	**Debit**	**Credit**

AP-8B (❸❹❺❻❼)

Presto Chango has the following adjustments to make at the end of December 2016, the end of its fiscal year.

Dec 31 Salaries accrued but not yet paid amount to $750.
Dec 31 Unearned revenue of $620 has now been earned.
Dec 31 A count of the office supplies shows that $320 worth still remains on hand.
Dec 31 Interest accrued on the bank loan but not yet paid amount to $70.
Dec 31 Monthly depreciation on equipment was $400.

Presto Chango Chart of Accounts (GL No.)

Account Description	Account #
ASSETS	
Cash	101
Accounts Receivable	105
Office Supplies	110
Equipment	120
Accumulated Depreciation—Equipment	130
LIABILITIES	
Accounts Payable	200
Unearned Revenue	205
Interest Payable	210
Salaries Payable	220
Bank Loan	225

Account Description	Account #
OWNER'S EQUITY	
Presto, Capital	300
Presto, Drawings	310
REVENUE	
Service Revenue	400
EXPENSES	
Salaries Expense	520
Depreciation Expense	525
Interest Expense	530
Supplies Expense	535

Required

a) Complete the six-column worksheet.
b) Journalize the adjustments.
c) Post the transactions to the general ledger accounts provided.

Presto Chango
Worksheet
December 31, 2016

	Unadjusted Trial Balance		Adjustments		Adjusted Trial Balance	
Account Titles	**DR**	**CR**	**DR**	**CR**	**DR**	**CR**
Cash	$4,200					
Accounts Receivable	1,350					
Office Supplies	680					
Equipment	14,500					
Accumulated Depreciation—Equipment		$800				
Accounts Payable		1,300				
Unearned Revenue		1,250				
Bank Loan		6,000				
Presto, Capital		4,880				
Presto, Drawings	800					
Service Revenue		8,700				
Salaries Expense	1,400					
Total	$22,930	$22,930				

JOURNAL				Page 2
Date	Account Titles and Explanation	PR	Debit	Credit

Account:					GL No:	
Date: 2016	Description	PR	DR	CR	Balance (DR or CR)	
	Opening Balance					

Account:					GL No:	
Date: 2016	Description	PR	DR	CR	Balance (DR or CR)	
	Opening Balance					

Account:					GL No:	
Date: 2016	Description	PR	DR	CR	Balance (DR or CR)	
	Opening Balance					

Account:					GL No:	
Date: 2016	Description	PR	DR	CR	Balance (DR or CR)	
	Opening Balance					

Account:					GL No:	
Date: 2016	Description	PR	DR	CR	Balance (DR or CR)	
	Opening Balance					

Account:					GL No:	
Date: 2016	Description	PR	DR	CR	Balance (DR or CR)	
	Opening Balance					

Account:					GL No:	
Date: 2016	Description	PR	DR	CR	Balance (DR or CR)	
	Opening Balance					

Account:					GL No:	
Date: 2016	Description	PR	DR	CR	Balance (DR or CR)	
	Opening Balance					

Account:					GL No:	
Date: 2016	Description	PR	DR	CR	Balance (DR or CR)	
	Opening Balance					

Account:					GL No:	
Date: 2016	Description	PR	DR	CR	Balance (DR or CR)	
	Opening Balance					

AP-9B (❻)

On January 1, 2016, Sokatoa, a carpet cleaning business, purchased a new machine for $60,000. The machine is expected to last six years and will have no residual value. Sokatoa has a December 31 year end. Prepare the table below showing the yearly depreciation, accumulated depreciation and net book value of the machine.

Year	Original Cost of Machine	Depreciation Expense	Accumulated Depreciation	Net Book Value
2016				
2017				
2018				
2019				
2020				
2021				
Total				

AP-10B (❻)

On November 1, 2016, Blue Skies Travel refurnished the entire office for $25,000. The furniture is expected to last four years and has an estimated residual value of $1,000. Blue Skies Travel has a December 31 year end. Prepare the table below showing the yearly depreciation, accumulated depreciation and net book value of the furniture.

Year	Original Cost of Furniture	Depreciation Expense	Accumulated Depreciation	Net Book Value
2016				
2017				
2018				
2019				
2020				
Total				

AP-11B (8)

On August 16, 2016, the bookkeeper for Wombat Eco-Adventure Tours discovered an error in the journal entries. On August 9, an entry was made to pay for a one-year insurance policy for $1,800, however accounts payable was used in error, instead of cash. Prepare the entries to correct this error.

JOURNAL				Page 2
Date	**Account Titles and Explanation**	**PR**	**Debit**	**Credit**

AP-12B (8)

On February 21, 2016, the bookkeeper for Crystal Clear, a pool cleaning business, discovered an error in the journal entries. On February 6, an entry was made to pay for repairs expense with $800 cash, however rent expense was debited in error. Prepare the entries to correct this error.

JOURNAL				Page 2
Date	**Account Titles and Explanation**	**PR**	**Debit**	**Credit**

Case Study

CS-1 (❷ ❸ ❹ ❺ ❻)

One Stop Event Planning is preparing year-end financial statements dated December 31, 2016 and has to make several adjustments before the financial statements can be prepared. The owner has approached the accountant with the following information.

1. A large contract worth a lot of money was started in November of this year that will be completed in early January. The customer will not pay until the contract is completed in January. The owner does not want to include any work already completed in revenue and would rather record the entire amount earned in January when the contract is complete.
2. Interest, utilities and salaries expense will be accrued on December 31, 2016. Utility bills are usually received on the 15th of the month and are usually the same amounts each month. The owner wants to accrue the full amount of the utilities on December 31, 2016 instead of just half that would normally be accrued.
3. An insurance policy was purchased in September covering one year. The owner wants to include the entire amount of the policy as an expense for the 2016 year end.
4. A customer paid a deposit in October for work to be completed in December and January. The initial receipt of cash was recorded in unearned revenue. The majority of the work was completed by December 31, 2016. The owner wants to wait until the work is 100% complete in January before recording any of it as revenue.
5. Equipment and furniture are depreciated using the straight-line method over five years. The owner wants to change the estimate from five years to three years for the depreciation calculation on December 31, 2016.

Required

a) For each action the owner wants, discover if there is any violation of ASPE principles or characteristics.

b) For each action the owner wants, identify how this would affect the financial statements.

c) What are some possible reasons the owner would want to make these changes to the adjustment process?

Chapter 6

THE ACCOUNTING CYCLE: STATEMENTS AND CLOSING ENTRIES

LEARNING OUTCOMES

❶ Prepare financial statements using the adjusted trial balance

❷ Prepare closing journal entries and post them to the general ledger

❸ Prepare the post-closing trial balance to complete the accounting cycle

❹ Distinguish between current and long-term assets and liabilities

❺ Prepare the classified balance sheet

❻ Calculate working capital, the current ratio and the quick ratio

❼ Describe the benefits of a computerized accounting system over a manual system

Appendix

❽ Prepare a 10-column worksheet

AMEENGAGE™ *Access **ameengage.com** for integrated resources including tutorials, practice exercises, the digital textbook and more.*

Assessment Questions

AS-1 (❶)

What does the income statement report?

____

____

AS-2 (❶)

Which statement is prepared after the income statement but before the balance sheet?

____

____

AS-3 (❶)

What does the statement of owner's equity report?

____

____

AS-4 (❶)

What two items cause owner's equity to increase and what two items cause owner's equity to decrease?

____

____

____

AS-5 (❶)

Which categories of accounts are reported on the balance sheet?

____

____

AS-6 (❶)

How does accumulated depreciation affect the value of property, plant and equipment?

____

____

AS-7 (❷)

What does it mean to close the books?

____

____

____

AS-8(❷)

What are the three steps to close directly to owner's capital?

____

____

____

AS-9 (❷)

What are the four steps to close the accounts using the income summary?

____

____

____

AS-10 (❷)

If a company has a net income for the period and closes its books using the income summary account, will the income summary account have a debit or credit balance before it is closed to the capital account?

____

____

AS-11 (❸)

Which categories of accounts appear on the post-closing trial balance?

____

____

AS-12 (❼)

Identify two benefits of a computerized accounting system.

____

____

____

AS-13 (❹)

Define current assets.

____

____

AS-14 (4)

Define long-term assets.

____

____

____

AS-15 (4)

What are current liabilities? Provide two examples of current liabilities.

____

____

____

AS-16 (4)

What are long-term liabilities? Provide two examples of long-term liabilities.

____

____

____

AS-17 (5)

What is one difference between a non-classified balance sheet and a classified balance sheet?

____

____

____

AS-18 (6)

How do you calculate the current ratio and what does it measure?

____

____

____

Application Questions Group A

AP-1A (❶)

Floating Speed Boat has completed all its journal entries and adjusting entries for the month of September 2016. The adjusted trial balance is shown below.

Note: During the month of September, the owner of Floating Speed Boat invested $6,900 into the business.

Floating Speed Boat Adjusted Trial Balance September 30, 2016		
Account Titles	**DR**	**CR**
Cash	$8,800	
Accounts Receivable	7,900	
Prepaid Insurance	1,150	
Equipment	64,000	
Accumulated Depreciation—Equipment		$1,260
Accounts Payable		9,900
Interest Payable		150
Unearned Revenue		5,930
Bank Loan		15,400
Murray, Capital		49,000
Murray, Drawings	1,200	
Service Revenue		3,970
Advertising Expense	430	
Depreciation Expense	390	
Insurance Expense	250	
Interest Expense	150	
Rent Expense	1,340	
Total	$85,610	$85,610

Required

Prepare the income statement, statement of owner's equity and the balance sheet from the adjusted trial balance.

AP-2A (❶❷❸)

Regina Restorations provides restorations for heritage buildings and has completed all its journal entries and adjusting entries for the year ended October 31, 2016. The adjusted trial balance is shown below.

Regina Restorations Adjusted Trial Balance October 31, 2016		
Account Titles	**DR**	**CR**
Cash	$32,000	
Accounts Receivable	9,500	
Prepaid Rent	4,680	
Equipment	15,000	
Accumulated Depreciation—Equipment		$1,290
Accounts Payable		27,800
Unearned Revenue		4,470
Bank Loan		1,600
Regina, Capital		9,330
Service Revenue		31,330
Depreciation Expense	340	
Insurance Expense	570	
Interest Expense	150	
Rent Expense	720	
Salaries Expense	6,400	
Supplies Expense	360	
Utilities Expense	6,100	
Total	$75,820	$75,820

Required

a) Prepare the income statement, statement of owner's equity and the balance sheet from the adjusted trial balance.
b) Create the closing entries using the income summary account.
c) Prepare the post-closing trial balance.

a) Prepare the financial statements.

b) Prepare the closing entries.

JOURNAL				Page 1
Date	Account Title and Explanation	PR	Debit	Credit

c) Prepare the post-closing trial balance.

Account Titles	DR	CR

AP-3A (❷ ❸)

Nichols Canoe Tours has journalized its adjusting entries and prepared its adjusted trial balance.

Nichols Canoe Tours Adjusted Trial Balance August 31, 2016		
Account Titles	**DR**	**CR**
Cash	$6,200	
Accounts Receivable	1,750	
Prepaid Insurance	1,650	
Office Supplies	1,150	
Equipment	10,650	
Accumulated Depreciation—Equipment		$320
Accounts Payable		1,640
Interest Payable		50
Unearned Revenue		1,420
Bank Loan		3,000
Nichols, Capital		14,290
Nichols, Drawings	2,000	
Service Revenue		4,100
Depreciation Expense	150	
Insurance Expense	170	
Interest Expense	50	
Rent Expense	800	
Telephone Expense	250	
Total	$24,820	$24,820

Required

a) Prepare the closing entries using the income summary account for the year ended August 31, 2016.
b) Prepare the post-closing trial balance.

a) Closing entries

JOURNAL				Page 1
Date	**Account Title and Explanation**	**PR**	**Debit**	**Credit**

b) Post-closing trial balance

Account Titles	**DR**	**CR**

AP-4A (❷ ❸)

Rejuvenation Spa, owned by Claire Sawyer, has journalized its adjusting entries and prepared its adjusted trial balance.

Rejuvenation Spa Adjusted Trial Balance October 31, 2016		
Account Titles	**DR**	**CR**
Cash	$8,620	
Accounts Receivable	2,340	
Prepaid Insurance	2,650	
Office Supplies	1,840	
Equipment	23,400	
Accumulated Depreciation—Equipment		$1,640
Accounts Payable		3,540
Interest Payable		120
Unearned Revenue		2,110
Bank Loan		5,500
Sawyer, Capital		24,080
Sawyer, Drawings	3,200	
Service Revenue		8,750
Depreciation Expense	260	
Insurance Expense	185	
Interest Expense	120	
Rent Expense	1,200	
Telephone Expense	275	
Salaries Expense	1,650	
Total	$45,740	$45,740

Required

a) Prepare the closing entries using the income summary account for the year ended October 31, 2016.

b) Prepare the post-closing trial balance.

a) Closing entries

JOURNAL				**Page 1**
Date	**Account Title and Explanation**	**PR**	**Debit**	**Credit**

b) Post-closing trial balance

Account Titles	**DR**	**CR**

AP-5A (❷ ❸)

Hotel Protector provides security services to the hotel industry and has journalized its adjusting entries and prepared its adjusted trial balance.

Hotel Protector **Adjusted Trial Balance** **December 31, 2016**		
Account Titles	**DR**	**CR**
Cash	$12,650	
Accounts Receivable	5,420	
Prepaid Insurance	2,820	
Office Supplies	2,240	
Equipment	25,600	
Accumulated Depreciation—Equipment		$2,340
Accounts Payable		6,250
Salaries Payable		650
Unearned Revenue		4,250
Bank Loan		7,500
Holmes, Capital		21,645
Holmes, Drawings	4,300	
Service Revenue		16,875
Depreciation Expense	320	
Insurance Expense	220	
Interest Expense	160	
Rent Expense	1,890	
Telephone Expense	350	
Salaries Expense	3,540	
Total	$59,510	$59,510

Required

a) Prepare the closing entries directly to owner's capital for the year ended December 31, 2016.

b) Prepare the post-closing trial balance.

a) Closing entries

JOURNAL				Page 1
Date	Account Title and Explanation	PR	Debit	Credit

b) Post-closing trial balance

Account Titles	DR	CR

AP-6A (❷ ❸)

Luminary Hotel has journalized its adjusting entries and prepared its adjusted trial balance.

Luminary Hotel Adjusted Trial Balance March 31, 2016		
Account Titles	**DR**	**CR**
Cash	$10,420	
Accounts Receivable	6,350	
Prepaid Insurance	2,350	
Office Supplies	1,860	
Equipment	32,500	
Accumulated Depreciation—Equipment		$5,480
Accounts Payable		4,870
Salaries Payable		840
Unearned Revenue		5,340
Bank Loan		9,000
Watts, Capital		23,745
Watts, Drawings	5,200	
Room Revenue		17,850
Depreciation Expense	410	
Insurance Expense	195	
Interest Expense	210	
Office Supplies Expense	670	
Rent Expense	2,150	
Telephone Expense	450	
Salaries Expense	4,360	
Total	$67,125	$67,125

Required

a) Prepare the closing entries directly to owner's capital for the year ended March 31, 2016.
b) Prepare the post-closing trial balance.

a) Closing entries

JOURNAL				**Page 1**
Date	**Account Title and Explanation**	**PR**	**Debit**	**Credit**

b) Post-closing trial balance

Account Titles	**DR**	**CR**

AP-7A (❶❷❸)

Evan's Events, owned by Evan Thompson, has completed all its journal entries and adjusting entries for the year ended April 30, 2016. The chart of accounts and adjusted trial balance are shown below.

Account Description	Account #
ASSETS	
Cash	101
Accounts Receivable	105
Prepaid Insurance	110
Equipment	120
Accumulated Depreciation—Equipment	125
LIABILITIES	
Accounts Payable	200
Unearned Revenue	210
Bank Loan	215
OWNER'S EQUITY	
Thompson, Capital	300
Thompson, Drawings	310
Income Summary	315

Account Description	Account #
REVENUE	
Service Revenue	400
EXPENSES	
Depreciation Expense	510
Insurance Expense	515
Interest Expense	520
Rent Expense	540
Salaries Expense	545
Telephone Expense	550
Travel Expense	555

Evan's Events
Adjusted Trial Balance
April 30, 2016

Account Titles	DR	CR
Cash	$32,050	
Accounts Receivable	9,000	
Prepaid Insurance	1,100	
Equipment	15,000	
Accumulated Depreciation—Equipment		$120
Accounts Payable		25,550
Unearned Revenue		3,200
Bank Loan		1,500
Thompson, Capital		18,000
Service Revenue		26,300
Depreciation Expense	120	
Insurance Expense	100	
Interest Expense	50	
Rent Expense	1,000	
Salaries Expense	8,000	
Telephone Expense	250	
Travel Expense	8,000	
Total	$74,670	$74,670

Required

a) Prepare the income statement, statement of owner's equity and the balance sheet.
b) Create the closing entries using the income summary account and post the closing entries to the ledger accounts. The ledger accounts are presented at the end of this question.
c) Prepare the post-closing trial balance.

Note: The daily transactions and adjustments for the month of April have already been posted in the general ledger. You are only responsible for posting the closing entries.

a) Prepare the financial statements.

b) Prepare the closing entries.

JOURNAL				Page 3
Date	Account Title and Explanation	PR	Debit	Credit

c) Prepare the post-closing trial balance.

Account Titles	DR	CR

GENERAL LEDGER

Account: Cash					GL. No: 101	
Date	Description	PR	DR	CR	Balance	
2016						
Apr 1	Opening Balance				22,000	DR
Apr 2		J1	25,000		47,000	DR
Apr 3		J1		1,000	46,000	DR
Apr 4		J1		1,200	44,800	DR
Apr 10		J1		200	44,600	DR
Apr 14		J1		8,000	36,600	DR
Apr 20		J1		50	36,550	DR
Apr 30		J1		4,500	32,050	DR

Account: Accounts Receivable					GL No: 105	
Date	Description	PR	DR	CR	Balance	
2016						
Apr 1	Opening Balance				9,000	DR

Account: Prepaid Insurance					GL No: 110	
Date	Description	PR	DR	CR	Balance	
2016						
Apr 1	Opening Balance				0	DR
Apr 4		J1	1,200		1,200	DR
Apr 30	Adjustment	J2		100	1,100	DR

Account: Equipment					GL No: 120	
Date	Description	PR	DR	CR	Balance	
2016						
Apr 1	Opening Balance				8,000	DR
Apr 1		J1	7,000		15,000	DR

Account: Accumulated Depreciation—Equipment					GL No: 125	
Date	Description	PR	DR	CR	Balance	
2016						
Apr 30	Adjustment	J2		120	120	CR

Account:	Accounts Payable				GL No: 200	
Date	**Description**	**PR**	**DR**	**CR**	**Balance**	
2016						
Apr 1	Opening Balance				10,500	CR
Apr 1		J1		7,000	17,500	CR
Apr 10		J1	200		17,300	CR
Apr 22		J1		250	17,550	CR
Apr 24		J1		8,000	25,550	CR

Account:	Unearned Revenue				GL No: 210	
Date	**Description**	**PR**	**DR**	**CR**	**Balance**	
2016						
Apr 1	Opening Balance				4,500	CR
Apr 30	Adjustment	J2	1,300		3,200	CR

Account:	Bank Loan				GL No: 215	
Date	**Description**	**PR**	**DR**	**CR**	**Balance**	
2016						
Apr 1	Opening Balance				6,000	CR
Apr 30		J1	4,500		1,500	CR

Account:	Thompson, Capital				GL No: 300	
Date	**Description**	**PR**	**DR**	**CR**	**Balance**	
2016						
Apr 1	Opening Balance				18,000	CR

Account:	Thompson, Drawings				GL No: 310	
Date	**Description**	**PR**	**DR**	**CR**	**Balance**	

Account: Income Summary					GL No: 315	
Date	**Description**	**PR**	**DR**	**CR**	**Balance**	

Account: Service Revenue					GL No: 400	
Date	**Description**	**PR**	**DR**	**CR**	**Balance**	
2016						
Apr 2		J1		25,000	25,000	CR
Apr 30	Adjustment	J2		1,300	26,300	CR

Account: Depreciation Expense					GL No: 510	
Date	**Description**	**PR**	**DR**	**CR**	**Balance**	
2016						
Apr 30	Adjustment	J2	120		120	DR

Account: Insurance Expense					GL No: 515	
Date	**Description**	**PR**	**DR**	**CR**	**Balance**	
2016						
Apr 30	Adjustment	J2	100		100	DR

Account: Interest Expense					GL No: 520	
Date	**Description**	**PR**	**DR**	**CR**	**Balance**	
2016						
Apr 20		J1	50		50	DR

Account: Rent Expense					GL No: 540	
Date	**Description**	**PR**	**DR**	**CR**	**Balance**	
2016						
Apr 3		J1	1,000		1,000	DR

Account: Salaries Expense					GL No: 545	
Date	**Description**	**PR**	**DR**	**CR**	**Balance**	
2016						
Apr 14		J1	8,000		8,000	DR

Account: Telephone Expense					GL No: 550	
Date	**Description**	**PR**	**DR**	**CR**	**Balance**	
2016						
Apr 22		J1	250		250	DR

Account: Travel Expense					GL No: 555	
Date	**Description**	**PR**	**DR**	**CR**	**Balance**	
2016						
Apr 24		J1	8,000		8,000	DR

AP-8A (❶ ❷ ❸)

Space Shuttle operates chartered shuttle buses between events and nearby hotels. Space Shuttle has already completed most of the transactions for the year and posted them to the general ledger. The following transactions during December 2016 have not yet been prepared.

Dec 2	Prepaid $12,000 for one year of insurance in advance.
Dec 5	Paid $1,400 cash for regular maintenance on shuttle buses.
Dec 12	The owner, Stephen Bugs, withdrew $3,500 cash from the business for personal use.
Dec 18	Received $2,200 cash deposit from a customer for future shuttle services.
Dec 23	Paid $1,000 to reduce the bank loan, of which $870 was principal and the rest was interest.
Dec 28	Received $450 cash from a customer who owed money for previous services.

Required

a) Prepare the journal entries for the above transactions.

JOURNAL				Page 1
Date	Account Title and Explanation	PR	Debit	Credit

b) Post the above journal entries to the general ledger. The chart of accounts is shown below for your reference.

Account Description	Account #
ASSETS	
Cash	101
Accounts Receivable	105
Prepaid Insurance	110
Equipment	120
Accumulated Depreciation—Equipment	125
LIABILITIES	
Accounts Payable	200
Salaries Payable	210
Unearned Revenue	220
Bank Loan	250

Account Description	Account #
OWNER'S EQUITY	
Bugs, Capital	300
Bugs, Drawings	310
Income Summary	315
REVENUE	
Service Revenue	400
EXPENSES	
Maintenance Expense	500
Depreciation Expense	520
Interest Expense	540
Insurance Expense	560
Salaries Expense	570

GENERAL LEDGER

Account:	**Cash**				**GL No: 101**	
Date	**Description**	**PR**	**DR**	**CR**	**Balance (DR or CR)**	
2016	Opening Balance				18,500	DR

Account:	**Accounts Receivable**				**GL No: 105**	
Date	**Description**	**PR**	**DR**	**CR**	**Balance (DR or CR)**	
2016	Opening Balance				3,200	DR

Account:	**Prepaid Insurance**				**GL No: 110**	
Date	**Description**	**PR**	**DR**	**CR**	**Balance (DR or CR)**	
2016	Opening Balance				1,000	DR

Account:	**Equipment**				**GL No: 120**	
Date	**Description**	**PR**	**DR**	**CR**	**Balance (DR or CR)**	
2016	Opening Balance				285,000	DR

Account:	Accumulated Depreciation—Equipment				GL No: 125	
Date	**Description**	**PR**	**DR**	**CR**	**Balance (DR or CR)**	
2016	Opening Balance				45,000	CR

Account:	Accounts Payable				GL No: 200	
Date	**Description**	**PR**	**DR**	**CR**	**Balance (DR or CR)**	
2016	Opening Balance				5,500	CR

Account:	Salaries Payable				GL No: 210	
Date	**Description**	**PR**	**DR**	**CR**	**Balance (DR or CR)**	
2016	Opening Balance				0	CR

Account:	Unearned Revenue				GL No: 220	
Date	**Description**	**PR**	**DR**	**CR**	**Balance (DR or CR)**	
2016	Opening Balance				1,400	CR

Account:	Bank Loan				GL No: 250	
Date	**Description**	**PR**	**DR**	**CR**	**Balance (DR or CR)**	
2016	Opening Balance				192,550	CR

Account:	Bugs, Capital				GL No: 300	
Date	**Description**	**PR**	**DR**	**CR**	**Balance (DR or CR)**	
2016	Opening Balance				46,200	CR

Account:	Bugs, Drawings				GL No: 310	
Date	**Description**	**PR**	**DR**	**CR**	**Balance (DR or CR)**	
2016	Opening Balance				10,000	DR

Account:	Income Summary				GL No: 315	
Date	**Description**	**PR**	**DR**	**CR**	**Balance (DR or CR)**	
2016	Opening Balance				0	CR

Account:	Service Revenue				GL No: 400	
Date	**Description**	**PR**	**DR**	**CR**	**Balance (DR or CR)**	
2016	Opening Balance				78,000	CR

Account:	Maintenance Expense				GL No: 500	
Date	**Description**	**PR**	**DR**	**CR**	**Balance (DR or CR)**	
2016	Opening Balance				3,800	DR

Account:	Depreciation Expense				GL No: 520	
Date	**Description**	**PR**	**DR**	**CR**	**Balance (DR or CR)**	
2016	Opening Balance				4,000	DR

Account:	Interest Expense				GL No: 540	
Date	**Description**	**PR**	**DR**	**CR**	**Balance (DR or CR)**	
2016	Opening Balance				1,150	DR

Account:	Insurance Expense				GL No: 560	
Date	**Description**	**PR**	**DR**	**CR**	**Balance (DR or CR)**	
2016	Opening Balance				11,000	DR

Account:	Salaries Expense				GL No: 570	
Date	**Description**	**PR**	**DR**	**CR**	**Balance (DR or CR)**	
2016	Opening Balance				31,000	DR

c) Prepare a six-column worksheet, starting with the account balances from the general ledger above. Space Shuttle had the following year-end adjustments.

Dec 31	Provided $1,500 worth of services to customer who paid in advance.
Dec 31	One month of insurance worth $1,000 has been used.
Dec 31	One month of depreciation is $500.
Dec 31	Accrued salaries owed to employees worth $3,370.

	Unadjusted Trial Balance		**Adjustments**		**Adjusted Trial Balance**	
Account Titles	**DR**	**CR**	**DR**	**CR**	**DR**	**CR**

d) Prepare the financial statements for Space Shuttle.

e) Record the journal entries for the adjusting and closing transactions. Use the income summary method. Post these entries in the general ledger above from part (b).

JOURNAL				**Page 2**
Date	**Account Title and Explanation**	**PR**	**Debit**	**Credit**

f) Prepare the post-closing trial balance for Space Shuttle.

Account Titles	**DR**	**CR**

Analysis

The accountant for Space Shuttle found that a journal entry back in November had been entered incorrectly. The account that should have been debited was credited and vice versa. Why wasn't this error detected during the preparation of trial balances and financial statements?

AP-9A (❹)

The following information is taken from the records of Ginger Cafe.

Accounts Payable	$19,000
Short-Term Investment	12,000
Land	52,000
Cash	23,000
Equipment	29,000
Loans Payable	30,000
Office Furniture	18,000
Prepaid Expense	9,000
Unearned Revenue	6,000

Required

a) Calculate total current assets.

b) Calculate total long-term assets.

c) Calculate total assets.

AP-10A (❹)

Suppose a business has a $400,000 long-term bank loan on December 31, 2016. The borrowing arrangement requires the business to pay $100,000 of this debt by September 2017. Show how the business will report both current and long-term liabilities on its December 31, 2016 balance sheet.

AP-11A (❹)

TRB Home Inspection borrowed a $1,000,000 interest-free bank loan on January 1, 2016. Payment is agreed to be made in four years in four equal annual installments. Calculate the current and long-term liabilities as at December 31 for the following years.

	As at December 31			
	2016	**2017**	**2018**	**2019**
Current portion of loan payable				
Long-term loan payable				

AP-12A (❹)

Renegade Landscaping's general ledger includes the following account balances on December 31, 2016.

Accounts Payable	$12,000
Interest Payable	3,000
Salaries Payable	2,000
Bank Loan	
Current Portion	10,000
Long-Term Portion	20,000

Required

a) Calculate current liabilities.

b) Calculate long-term liabilities.

AP-13A (❹)

For the following independent transactions, determine the amount of current and long-term liabilities.

	Transaction	Current Liability	Long-Term Liability
1.	On December 31, 2016, Frankie Flowershop borrowed $300,000 from the bank. The entire amount is due on December 30, 2017.		
2.	KLM Company purchased a small building at a cost of $190,000. The down payment is $100,000. The remaining balance is payable in three years with an annual payment of $30,000, starting next year.		
3.	During June 2016, a business owner obtained an interest-free loan from a financing company. The loan amount was $60,000. The agreed terms of payment is four annual installments of $15,000.		
4.	A business owner borrowed $20,000 from his close friend for a business expansion. They both signed an agreement that the payment will be made after two years.		

AP-14A (❹ ❺ ❻)

Empowered Spa has the following balances as at May 31, 2016.

Cash	$22,000
Accounts Receivable	15,000
Inventory	12,000
Equipment	73,000
Accounts Payable	13,000
Unearned Revenue	8,000
Current Portion of Bank Loan	10,000
Long-Term Portion of Bank Loan	20,000
Powers, Capital	71,000

Required

a) Prepare a classified balance sheet using the balances listed above.

b) Calculate the working capital for Empowered Spa.

---

c) Calculate the current ratio for Empowered Spa.

---

d) Calculate the quick ratio for Empowered Spa.

AP-15A (❹ ❺ ❻)

Below is Preston Services' financial accounting information for the year ending September 30, 2016. Assume all accounts have a normal balance.

Cash	$7,500
Accounts Receivable	2,400
Inventory	6,000
Prepaid Insurance	1,800
Equipment	35,000
Accumulated Depreciation—Equipment	800
Accounts Payable	5,100
Unearned Revenue	1,100
Bank Loan	18,000
Preston, Capital	27,700

The bank loan is payable over 3 years and $6,000 will be paid by September 30, 2017.

Required

a) Prepare a classified balance sheet.

b) Calculate the working capital for Preston Services.

---

c) Calculate the current ratio for Preston Services.

---

d) Calculate the quick ratio for Preston Services.

AP-16A (❽)

Below, is Coleson Services' unadjusted trial balance at the end of December 2016. Adjusting entries have not yet been made. Use the trial balance and the information below to complete the worksheet.

Dec 31	A physical count showed that $320 of supplies is still on hand.
Dec 31	The equipment was purchased at the beginning of the year and is expected to last four years and no residual value.
Dec 31	Of the balance of unearned revenue, $600 has been earned.
Dec 31	The amount in prepaid insurance is for an annual policy that was paid on September 1, 2016.

Coleson Services Worksheet December 31, 2016										
	Unadjusted Trial Balance		Adjustments		Adjusted Trial Balance		Income Statement		Balance Sheet	
Account Titles	**DR**	**CR**	**DR**	**CR**	**DR**	**CR**	**DR**	**CR**	**DR**	**CR**
Cash	$1,500									
Accounts Receivable	3,000									
Prepaid Insurance	1,800									
Office Supplies	800									
Equipment	6,000									
Accumulated Depreciation—Equipment		$0								
Accounts Payable		4,000								
Unearned Revenue		1,000								
Bank Loan		2,500								
Coleson, Capital		2,850								
Coleson, Drawings	1,200									
Service Revenue		8,000								
Depreciation Expense	0									
Insurance Expense	0									
Interest Expense	0									
Maintenance Expense	900									
Supplies Expense	0									
Rent Expense	1,900									
Salaries Expense	150									
Telephone Expense	700									
Travel Expense	400									
Total	$18,350	$18,350								
Net Income										
Total										

Application Questions Group B

AP-1B (❶)

Below is Caprio Catering's adjusted trial balance for the year ending December 31, 2016. Using this information, prepare the income statement, statement of owner's equity and then the balance sheet for the end of December 31, 2016.

Caprio Catering Adjusted Trial Balance December 31, 2016		
Account Titles	**DR**	**CR**
Cash	$90,200	
Accounts Receivable	47,800	
Prepaid Insurance	32,000	
Equipment	415,000	
Accumulated Depreciation—Equipment		$145,000
Accounts Payable		26,000
Unearned Revenue		15,800
Bank Loan		260,000
Caprio, Capital		108,200
Caprio, Drawings	40,000	
Service Revenue		545,000
Advertising Expense	100,000	
Insurance Expense	40,000	
Maintenance Expense	5,900	
Rent Expense	78,000	
Salaries Expense	228,500	
Telephone Expense	3,200	
Travel Expense	19,400	
Total	**$1,100,000**	**$1,100,000**

Note: During the year, the owner contributed $20,000 to the business. This has been included in Caprio, Capital already.

Analysis

In the accounting cycle, why is the income statement prepared first, then the statement of owner's equity, and finally the balance sheet?

AP-2B (➊)

Counterpoint Studios has completed all the entries for the month of November 2016, except the monthly adjusting entries. The following information is available to make the adjustments.

- Annual depreciation on property, plant, and equipment totals $9,000.
- Interest accrued on the bank loan is $500.
- Office supplies on hand are valued at $2,300.
- The annual insurance policy was purchased December 1, 2015 for $21,900.
- The balance of owner's equity at the beginning of November was $86,750.

Required

a) Complete the six-column worksheet for Counterpoint Studios.

Counterpoint Studios Worksheet November 30, 2016						
	Unadjusted Trial Balance		Adjustments		Adjusted Trial Balance	
Account Titles	**DR**	**CR**	**DR**	**CR**	**DR**	**CR**
Cash	$52,250					
Accounts Receivable	24,800					
Office Supplies	10,400					
Prepaid Insurance	1,825					
Equipment	295,400					
Accumulated Depreciation—Equipment		$107,250				
Accounts Payable		31,500				
Bank Loan		140,000				
Wu, Capital		96,750				
Wu, Drawings	60,000					
Service Revenue		382,500				
Advertising Expense	100,000					
Salaries Expense	185,000					
Insurance Expense	20,075					
Depreciation Expense	8,250					
Total	$758,000	$758,000				

b) Prepare the income statement, statement of owner's equity and balance sheet.

AP-3B (❷ ❸)

Jim's Custom Catering has journalized its adjusting entries and prepared its adjusted trial balance.

Jim's Custom Catering Adjusted Trial Balance August 31, 2016		
Account Titles	**DR**	**CR**
Cash	$8,400	
Accounts Receivable	2,900	
Prepaid Rent	2,100	
Office Supplies	2,400	
Equipment	20,700	
Accumulated Depreciation—Equipment		$2,700
Accounts Payable		3,200
Interest Payable		300
Unearned Revenue		2,900
Mortgage Payable		5,400
Gordon, Capital		22,360
Gordon, Drawings	4,000	
Service Revenue		7,600
Depreciation Expense	150	
Insurance Expense	240	
Interest Expense	300	
Rent Expense	1,420	
Supplies Expense	350	
Travel Expense	1,500	
Total	$44,460	$44,460

Required

a) Prepare the closing entries using the income summary account for the year ended August 31, 2016.

b) Prepare the post-closing trial balance.

a) Closing entries

JOURNAL				Page 1
Date	**Account Title and Explanation**	**PR**	**Debit**	**Credit**

b) Post-closing trial balance

Account Titles	**DR**	**CR**

AP-4B (❷)

Portal Delivery Services has prepared its income statement and statement of owner's equity.

Portal Delivery Services **Income Statement** **For the Year Ended October 31, 2016**		
Service Revenue		$500,000
Expenses		
Transportation Expense	$95,000	
Salaries Expense	240,000	
Maintenance Expense	70,000	
Depreciation Expense	45,000	
Total Expenses		450,000
Net Income (Loss)		$50,000

Portal Delivery Services Statement of Owner's Equity For the Year Ended October 31, 2016		
Jones, Capital at November 1, 2015		$120,000
Add		
Additional Investments	$30,000	
Net Income (Loss)	50,000	80,000
Subtotal		200,000
Less		
Jones, Drawings		100,000
Jones, Capital at October 31, 2016		$100,000

Required

Prepare the closing entries using the income summary method for Portal Delivery Services.

JOURNAL				Page 1
Date	**Account Title and Explanation**	**PR**	**Debit**	**Credit**

Analysis

What is the purpose of preparing closing entries at the end of each period? Explain.

____

____

____

____

____

AP-5B (❷ ❸)

Hotel Security has journalized its adjusting entries and prepared its adjusted trial balance.

Hotel Security Adjusted Trial Balance January 31, 2016		
Account Titles	**DR**	**CR**
Cash	$14,200	
Accounts Receivable	6,900	
Prepaid Services	4,000	
Office Supplies	2,000	
Equipment	37,700	
Accumulated Depreciation—Equipment		$5,700
Accounts Payable		4,800
Salaries Payable		950
Unearned Revenue		4,800
Mortgage Payable		8,800
Sherlock, Capital		32,750
Sherlock, Drawings	4,900	
Service Revenue		18,200
Depreciation Expense	350	
Insurance Expense	290	
Maintenance Expense	470	
Rent Expense	1,500	
Telephone Expense	490	
Utilities Expense	3,200	
Total	$76,000	$76,000

Required

a) Prepare the closing entries directly to owner's capital for the year ended January 31, 2016.
b) Prepare the post-closing trial balance.

a) Closing entries

JOURNAL				Page 1
Date	**Account Title and Explanation**	**PR**	**Debit**	**Credit**

b) Post-closing trial balance

Account Titles	**DR**	**CR**

AP-6B (❷ ❸)

Health Foods has journalized its adjusting entries and prepared its adjusted trial balance.

Health Foods Adjusted Trial Balance May 31, 2016		
Account Titles	**DR**	**CR**
Cash	$14,800	
Accounts Receivable	7,600	
Prepaid Rent	3,300	
Office Supplies	2,300	
Equipment	39,300	
Accumulated Depreciation—Equipment		$5,200
Accounts Payable		4,200
Salaries Payable		980
Unearned Revenue		4,800
Mortgage Payable		11,000
Schmitt, Capital		34,820
Schmitt, Drawings	4,400	
Service Revenue		17,000
Depreciation Expense	140	
Insurance Expense	140	
Maintenance Expense	160	
Office Supplies Expense	880	
Rent Expense	1,400	
Telephone Expense	280	
Utilities Expense	3,300	
Total	$78,000	$78,000

Required

a) Prepare the closing entries directly to owner's capital for the year ended May 31, 2016.

b) Prepare the post-closing trial balance.

a) Closing entries

JOURNAL				**Page 1**
Date	**Account Title and Explanation**	**PR**	**Debit**	**Credit**

b) Post-closing trial balance

Account Titles	**DR**	**CR**

AP-7B (❶❷❸)

High Flying Biplane has completed all its journal entries and adjusting entries for the year ended June 30, 2016. The chart of accounts and adjusted trial balance are shown below.

Account Description	Account #
ASSETS	
Cash	101
Accounts Receivable	105
Prepaid Insurance	110
Equipment	120
Accumulated Depreciation—Equipment	125
LIABILITIES	
Accounts Payable	200
Interest Payable	205
Unearned Revenue	210
Bank Loan	215
OWNER'S EQUITY	
Bridges, Capital	300
Bridges, Drawings	310
Income Summary	315

Account Description	Account #
REVENUE	
Service Revenue	400
EXPENSES	
Advertising Expense	500
Depreciation Expense	510
Insurance Expense	515
Interest Expense	520
Telephone Expense	550

High Flying Biplane
Adjusted Trial Balance
June 30, 2016

Account Titles	DR	CR
Cash	$8,800	
Accounts Receivable	6,800	
Prepaid Insurance	1,100	
Equipment	64,000	
Accumulated Depreciation—Equipment		$450
Accounts Payable		7,700
Interest Payable		75
Unearned Revenue		4,080
Bank Loan		19,000
Bridges, Capital		48,800
Bridges, Drawings	1,200	
Service Revenue		3,020
Advertising Expense	400	
Depreciation Expense	450	
Insurance Expense	100	
Interest Expense	75	
Telephone Expense	200	
Total	$83,125	$83,125

Required

a) Prepare the income statement, statement of owner's equity and the balance sheet.
b) Create the closing entries using the income summary account and post the closing entries to the ledger accounts.
c) Prepare the post-closing trial balance.

Note: The daily transactions and adjustments for the month of June have already been posted in the general ledger. You are only responsible for posting the closing entries.

a) Prepare financial statements.

b) Prepare the closing entries.

JOURNAL				Page 3
Date	**Account Title and Explanation**	**PR**	**Debit**	**Credit**

c) Prepare the post-closing trial balance.

Account Titles	**DR**	**CR**

GENERAL LEDGER

Account: Cash					GL. No: 101	
Date	**Description**	**PR**	**DR**	**CR**	**Balance**	
2015						
Jul 1	Opening Balance				8,000	DR
2016						
Jun 1		J1	5,000		13,000	DR
Jun 2		J1	1,500		14,500	DR
Jun 4		J1		200	14,300	DR
Jun 14		J1		4,000	10,300	DR
Jun 20		J1	1,600		11,900	DR
Jun 22		J1		900	11,000	DR
Jun 24		J1		1,000	10,000	DR
Jun 30		J1		1,200	8,800	DR

Account: Accounts Receivable					GL No: 105	
Date	**Description**	**PR**	**DR**	**CR**	**Balance**	
2015						
Jul 1	Opening Balance				6,000	DR
2016						
Jun 10		J1	2,400		8,400	DR
Jun 20		J1		1,600	6,800	DR

Account: Prepaid Insurance					GL No: 110	
Date	**Description**	**PR**	**DR**	**CR**	**Balance**	
2015						
Jul 1	Opening Balance				1,200	DR
2016						
Jun 30	Adjustment	J2		100	1,100	DR

Account: Equipment					GL No: 120	
Date	**Description**	**PR**	**DR**	**CR**	**Balance**	
2015						
Jul 1	Opening Balance				60,000	DR
2016						
Jun 14		J1	4,000		64,000	DR

Account: Accumulated Depreciation—Equipment					GL No: 125	
Date	**Description**	**PR**	**DR**	**CR**	**Balance**	
2016						
Jun 30	Adjustment	J2		450	450	CR

Account:	Accounts Payable				GL No: 200	
Date	Description	PR	DR	CR	Balance	
2015						
Jul 1	Opening Balance				8,200	CR
2016						
Jun 3		J1		400	8,600	CR
Jun 22		J1	900		7,700	CR

Account:	Interest Payable				GL No: 205	
Date	Description	PR	DR	CR	Balance	
2016						
Jun 30	Adjustment	J2		75	75	CR

Account:	Unearned Revenue				GL No: 210	
Date	Description	PR	DR	CR	Balance	
2015						
Jul 1	Opening Balance				3,200	CR
2016						
Jun 2		J1		1,500	4,700	CR
Jun 30	Adjustment	J2	620		4,080	CR

Account:	Bank Loan				GL No: 215	
Date	Description	PR	DR	CR	Balance	
2015						
Jul 1	Opening Balance				20,000	CR
2016						
Jun 24		J1	1,000		19,000	CR

Account:	Bridges, Capital				GL No: 300	
Date	Description	PR	DR	CR	Balance	
2015						
Jul 1	Opening Balance				43,800	CR
2016						
Jun 1		J1		5,000	48,800	CR

Account:	Bridges, Drawings				GL No: 310	
Date	Description	PR	DR	CR	Balance	
2016						
Jun 30		J1	1,200		1,200	DR

Account:	Income Summary				GL No: 315	
Date	Description	PR	DR	CR	Balance	

Account:	Service Revenue				GL No: 400	
Date	Description	PR	DR	CR	Balance	
2016						
Jun 10		J1		2,400	2,400	CR
Jun 30	Adjustment	J2		620	3,020	CR

Account:	Advertising Expense				GL No: 500	
Date	Description	PR	DR	CR	Balance	
2016						
Jun 3		J1	400		400	DR

Account:	Depreciation Expense				GL No: 510	
Date	Description	PR	DR	CR	Balance	
2016						
Jun 30	Adjustment	J2	450		450	DR

Account: Insurance Expense					GL No: 515	
Date	**Description**	**PR**	**DR**	**CR**	**Balance**	
2016						
Jun 30	Adjustment	J2	100		100	DR

Account: Interest Expense					GL No: 520	
Date	**Description**	**PR**	**DR**	**CR**	**Balance**	
2016						
Jun 30	Adjustment	J2	75		75	DR

Account: Telephone Expense					GL No: 550	
Date	**Description**	**PR**	**DR**	**CR**	**Balance**	
2016						
Jun 4		J1	200		200	DR

AP-8B (❶❷❸)

Patel Linens provides linen services to the hotel industry and has completed all its journal entries and adjusting entries for the year ended September 30, 2016. The chart of accounts and adjusted trial balance are shown below.

Account Description	Account #
ASSETS	
Cash	101
Accounts Receivable	105
Prepaid Insurance	110
Office Supplies	115
Equipment	120
Accumulated Depreciation—Equipment	125
LIABILITIES	
Accounts Payable	200
Unearned Revenue	210
Bank Loan	215
OWNER'S EQUITY	
Patel, Capital	300
Patel, Drawings	310
Income Summary	315

Account Description	Account #
REVENUE	
Service Revenue	400
EXPENSES	
Depreciation Expense	510
Insurance Expense	515
Interest Expense	520
Office Supplies Expense	530
Rent Expense	540

Patel Linens Adjusted Trial Balance September 30, 2016		
Account Titles	**DR**	**CR**
Cash	$5,800	
Accounts Receivable	1,450	
Prepaid Insurance	1,650	
Office Supplies	650	
Equipment	9,300	
Accumulated Depreciation—Equipment		$120
Accounts Payable		3,050
Unearned Revenue		1,040
Bank Loan		4,640
Patel, Capital		11,450
Patel, Drawings	1,600	
Service Revenue		2,260
Depreciation Expense	120	
Insurance Expense	150	
Interest Expense	40	
Office Supplies Expense	450	
Rent Expense	1,350	
Total	$22,560	$22,560

Required

a) Prepare the income statement, statement of owner's equity and the balance sheet.
b) Create the closing entries using the income summary account and post the closing entries to the ledger accounts.
c) Prepare the post-closing trial balance.

Note: The daily transactions and adjustments for the month of September have already been posted in the general ledger. You are only responsible for posting the closing entries.

a) Prepare the financial statements.

b) Prepare the closing entries.

JOURNAL				Page 3
Date	**Account Title and Explanation**	**PR**	**Debit**	**Credit**

c) Prepare the post-closing trial balance.

Account Titles	**DR**	**CR**

GENERAL LEDGER

Account: Cash					GL. No: 101	
Date	**Description**	**PR**	**DR**	**CR**	**Balance**	
2015						
Oct 1	Opening Balance				7,200	DR
2016						
Sep 1		J1		1,800	5,400	DR
Sep 2		J1	1,900		7,300	DR
Sep 3		J1		1,350	5,950	DR
Sep 10		J1		40	5,910	DR
Sep 10		J1		960	4,950	DR
Sep 20		J1	2,200		7,150	DR
Sep 22		J1	850		8,000	DR
Sep 24		J1		600	7,400	DR
Sep 30		J1		1,600	5,800	DR

Account: Accounts Receivable					GL No: 105	
Date	**Description**	**PR**	**DR**	**CR**	**Balance**	
2015						
Oct 1	Opening Balance				2,300	DR
2016						
Sep 22		J1		850	1,450	DR

Account: Prepaid Insurance					GL No: 110	
Date	**Description**	**PR**	**DR**	**CR**	**Balance**	
2015						
Oct 1	Opening Balance				0	DR
2016						
Sep 1		J1	1,800		1,800	DR
Sep 30	Adjustment	J2		150	1,650	DR

Account: Office Supplies					GL No: 115	
Date	**Description**	**PR**	**DR**	**CR**	**Balance**	
2015						
Oct 1	Opening Balance				850	DR
2016						
Sep 4		J1	250		1,100	DR
Sep 30	Adjustment	J2		450	650	DR

Account: Equipment					GL No: 120	
Date	**Description**	**PR**	**DR**	**CR**	**Balance**	
2015						
Oct 1	Opening Balance				11,500	DR
2016						
Sep 20		J1		2,200	9,300	DR

Account: Accumulated Depreciation—Equipment					GL No: 125	
Date	**Description**	**PR**	**DR**	**CR**	**Balance**	
2016						
Sep 30	Adjustment	J2		120	120	CR

Account: Accounts Payable					GL No: 200	
Date	**Description**	**PR**	**DR**	**CR**	**Balance**	
2015						
Oct 1	Opening Balance				3,400	CR
2016						
Sep 4		J1		250	3,650	CR
Sep 24		J1	600		3,050	CR

Account: Unearned Revenue					GL No: 210	
Date	**Description**	**PR**	**DR**	**CR**	**Balance**	
2015						
Oct 1	Opening Balance				1,400	CR
2016						
Sep 30	Adjustment	J2	360		1,040	CR

Account: Bank Loan					GL No: 215	
Date	**Description**	**PR**	**DR**	**CR**	**Balance**	
2015						
Oct 1	Opening Balance				5,600	CR
2016						
Sep 10		J1	960		4,640	CR

Account: Patel, Capital					GL No: 300	
Date	**Description**	**PR**	**DR**	**CR**	**Balance**	
2015						
Oct 1	Opening Balance				11,450	CR
2016						

Account:	Patel, Drawings				GL No: 310	
Date	Description	PR	DR	CR	Balance	
2016						
Sep 30		J1	1,600		1,600	DR

Account:	Income Summary				GL No: 315	
Date	Description	PR	DR	CR	Balance	

Account:	Service Revenue				GL No: 400	
Date	Description	PR	DR	CR	Balance	
2016						
Sep 2		J1		1,900	1,900	CR
Sep 30	Adjustment	J2		360	2,260	CR

Account:	Depreciation Expense				GL No: 510	
Date	Description	PR	DR	CR	Balance	
2016						
Sep 30	Adjustment	J2	120		120	DR

Account:	Insurance Expense				GL No: 515	
Date	Description	PR	DR	CR	Balance	
2016						
Sep 30	Adjustment	J2	150		150	DR

Account:	Interest Expense				GL No: 520	
Date	Description	PR	DR	CR	Balance	
2016						
Sep 10		J1	40		40	DR

Account:	Office Supplies Expense				GL No: 530	
Date	**Description**	**PR**	**DR**	**CR**	**Balance**	
2016						
Sep 30	Adjustment	J2	450		450	DR

Account:	Rent Expense				GL No: 540	
Date	**Description**	**PR**	**DR**	**CR**	**Balance**	
2016						
Sep 3		J1	1,350		1,350	DR

AP-9B (❹)

The following information is taken from the records of Basil Cleaning.

Accounts Payable	$18,000
Inventory	14,000
Land	55,000
Cash	31,000
Factory Equipment	20,000
Current Loans Payable	21,000
Office Furniture	18,000
Prepaid Insurance	13,000
Unearned Revenue	8,000

Required

a) Calculate total current assets.

b) Calculate total long-term assets.

c) Calculate total assets.

___

___

AP-10B (④)

Nylah's Resort borrowed a $1,180,000 interest-free bank loan on January 1, 2016. Payment is agreed to be made in four years in four equal annual instalments (paid on each subsequent January 1). Calculate the current and long-term liabilities as at December 31 before the annual instalments are made for the following years.

	December 31			
	2016	2017	2018	2019
Current portion of loan				
Long-term portion of loan				

AP-11B (④)

On July 1, 2016, Bryte Services took out a $200,000 bank loan. The loan will be repaid in equal annual installments over the next 10 years. Show how the bank loan will appear on Bryte Services' classified balance sheet on June 30, 2022.

___

___

___

Analysis

Show the journal entries required to record the receipt of the loan and the first principal payment.

JOURNAL				Page 1
Date	Account Title and Explanation	PR	Debit	Credit

AP-12B (❹)

On January 1, 2016, Baylis DJ Services took out a $100,000 bank loan. The loan will be repaid in two equal payments; one on December 31, 2017, and the other on December 31, 2019. Complete the table below with the correct balances for the accounts at the dates listed.

	Bank Loan	
	Current	**Long-Term**
Dec. 31, 2016		
Dec. 31, 2017		
Dec. 31, 2018		
Dec. 31, 2019		

Analysis

Why is it helpful to split some liabilities into current and long-term portions for reporting purposes?

____

____

____

____

____

AP-13B (❹)

Identify the following accounts as either current or long-term, and as either assets or liabilities.

Account Name	**Current or Long-Term**	**Asset or Liability**
Accounts Receivable		
Salaries Payable		
Equipment		
Cash		
Bank Loan due in six months		
Office Furniture		
Accounts Payable		
Prepaid Rent		
Bank Loan due in two years		
Inventory		

AP-14B (❹ ❺ ❻)

Below is Bravolo's adjusted trial balance for the year ending September 30, 2016. Assume all accounts have a normal balance.

Cash	$17,400
Accounts Receivable	5,800
Prepaid Insurance	1,800
Equipment	23,000
Accumulated Depreciation—Equipment	1,100
Accounts Payable	7,600
Unearned Revenue	1,500
Bank Loan	18,000
Bravolo, Capital	19,800

The bank loan is payable over three years and $6,000 will be paid by September 30, 2017.

Required

a) Prepare a classified balance sheet.

b) Calculate the working capital for Bravolo.

____

____

c) Calculate the current ratio for Bravolo.

____

____

d) Calculate the quick ratio for Bravolo.

____

____

AP-15B (❹ ❺ ❻)

Below is Canduro's financial information for the year ending June 30, 2016. Assume all accounts have a normal balance.

Accounts Payable	$8,900
Accounts Receivable	6,100
Accumulated Depreciation—Equipment	1,200
Bank Loan	21,000
Cash	19,000
Prepaid Insurance	3,250
Equipment	25,000
Canduro, Capital	20,550
Unearned Revenue	1,700

The bank loan is payable over five years and $4,200 will be paid by June 30, 2017.

Required

a) Prepare a classified balance sheet.

b) Calculate the working capital for Canduro.

____

c) Calculate the current ratio for Canduro.

____

d) Calculate the quick ratio for Canduro.

____

AP-16B (8)

Charles Ly is the owner of Gamma Travel. He has hired you to prepare the financial statements for his company on April 30, 2016. As part of the process, you need to create the worksheet. Use the unadjusted trial balance and the adjustments to complete the worksheet.

Apr 30 Recognized prepaid insurance worth $100 for this month.
Apr 30 Recorded $400 deprecation on equipment.
Apr 30 Recognized $1,800 of unearned revenue that has now become earned.

Gamma Travel Worksheet April 30, 2016										
	Unadjusted Trial Balance		Adjustments		Adjusted Trial Balance		Income Statement		Balance Sheet	
Account Titles	**DR**	**CR**	**DR**	**CR**	**DR**	**CR**	**DR**	**CR**	**DR**	**CR**
Cash	$21,750									
Accounts Receivable	13,000									
Prepaid Insurance	1,200									
Equipment	17,500									
Accumulated Depreciation—Equipment		$2,000								
Accounts Payable		10,300								
Unearned Revenue		4,500								
Bank Loan		18,000								
Ly, Capital		14,000								
Service Revenue		9,000								
Insurance Expense	0									
Salaries Expense	4,000									
Telephone Expense	200									
Depreciation Expense	0									
Interest Expense	150									
Totals	$57,800	$57,800								
Net Profit (Loss)										
Total										

Case Study

CS-1 (❶❷❸❹❺)

Snap App designs tailor-made mobile reservation applications for hotel chains. Its balance sheet at the end of June 2016 is shown below, along with its chart of accounts.

Snap App
Balance Sheet
As at June 30, 2016

Assets		**Liabilities**	
Cash	$7,580	Accounts Payable	$15,800
Accounts Receivable	6,000	Unearned Revenue	6,200
Prepaid Insurance	1,800	Bank Loan	22,000
Equipment	55,000	Total Liabilities	44,000
		Owner's Equity	
		Stone, Capital	26,380
Total Assets	$70,380	**Total Liabilities and Owner's Equity**	$70,380

Account Description	Account #
ASSETS	
Cash	101
Accounts Receivable	105
Prepaid Insurance	110
Equipment	120
Accumulated Depreciation—Equipment	125
LIABILITIES	
Accounts Payable	200
Interest Payable	205
Salary Payable	210
Unearned Revenue	215
Bank Loan	220
OWNER'S EQUITY	
Stone, Capital	300
Stone, Drawings	310
Income Summary	315

Account Description	Account #
REVENUE	
Service Revenue	400
EXPENSES	
Advertising Expense	500
Depreciation Expense	510
Insurance Expense	515
Interest Expense	520
Salaries Expense	545
Telephone Expense	550

For the month of July 2016, Snap App had the following transactions.

Jul 1	The owner invested $8,000 cash into the business.
Jul 2	Received $2,530 cash for work that will be provided in August.
Jul 5	Received an advertising bill for $600 which will be paid next month.
Jul 8	Paid the $350 telephone bill with cash.
Jul 10	Provided $4,680 worth of services to customers who will pay later.
Jul 14	Purchased equipment with $8,200 cash.
Jul 20	Received $2,350 in payment from customers paying their account.
Jul 22	Paid $1,970 toward accounts payable.
Jul 24	Paid $1,300 toward bank loan principal.
Jul 28	Paid salary of $2,400 to an employee.
Jul 30	The owner withdrew $2,200 cash for personal use.

At the end of July, the following adjustments had to be journalized to properly report the balances of the company's accounts.

Jul 31	One month of prepaid insurance worth $100 has been used.
Jul 31	Monthly depreciation on the equipment was $450.
Jul 31	Unearned revenue worth $620 has now been earned.
Jul 31	Interest of $75 has accrued on the bank loan.
Jul 31	Accrued salary expense of $500 for an employee.

Note: Of the remaining balance of the bank loan, $5,000 will be paid within the next year.

Required

a) Enter the opening balances from the June 2016 balance sheet into the general ledger accounts (the ledger accounts are presented at the end of this question).
b) Prepare the journal entries for the month of July and post them to the appropriate general ledger accounts.
c) Create the trial balance in the worksheet and then complete the remaining section of the worksheet.
d) Create the income statement, statement of owner's equity and the classified balance sheet.
e) Prepare the journal entries for the adjustments and post them to the appropriate general ledger accounts.
f) Prepare the journal entries to close the books for the month of July 2016 (use the income summary account), and post the journal entries to the appropriate general ledger accounts.
g) Create the post-closing trial balance.

a) Enter opening balances in the ledgers located at the end of the question.

b) Journal entries

JOURNAL				Page 1
Date	**Account Title and Explanation**	**PR**	**Debit**	**Credit**

c) Worksheet

	Unadjusted Trial Balance		**Adjustments**		**Adjusted Trial Balance**	
Account Titles	**DR**	**CR**	**DR**	**CR**	**DR**	**CR**

d) Financial statements

e) Adjusting entries

JOURNAL				Page 2
Date	**Account Title and Explanation**	**PR**	**Debit**	**Credit**

f) Closing entries

JOURNAL				Page 3
Date	Account Title and Explanation	PR	Debit	Credit

g) Create the post-closing trial balance.

Account Titles	**DR**	**CR**

GENERAL LEDGER

Account: Cash					**GL. No.**	
Date	**Description**	**PR**	**DR**	**CR**	**Balance**	

Account:					GL. No.	
Date	Description	PR	DR	CR	Balance	

Account:					GL. No.	
Date	Description	PR	DR	CR	Balance	

Account:					GL. No.	
Date	Description	PR	DR	CR	Balance	

Account:					GL. No.	
Date	Description	PR	DR	CR	Balance	

Account:					GL. No.	
Date	Description	PR	DR	CR	Balance	

Account:					GL. No.	
Date	Description	PR	DR	CR	Balance	

Account:					GL. No.	
Date	Description	PR	DR	CR	Balance	

Account:					GL. No.	
Date	Description	PR	DR	CR	Balance	

Account:					GL. No.	
Date	Description	PR	DR	CR	Balance	

Account:					GL. No.	
Date	Description	PR	DR	CR	Balance	

Account:					GL. No.	
Date	Description	PR	DR	CR	Balance	

Account:					GL. No.	
Date	Description	PR	DR	CR	Balance	

Account:					GL. No.	
Date	Description	PR	DR	CR	Balance	

Account:					GL. No.	
Date	Description	PR	DR	CR	Balance	

Account:					GL. No.	
Date	Description	PR	DR	CR	Balance	

Account:					GL. No.	
Date	Description	PR	DR	CR	Balance	

Account:					GL. No.	
Date	Description	PR	DR	CR	Balance	

Account:					GL. No.	
Date	Description	PR	DR	CR	Balance	

Account:					GL. No.	
Date	Description	PR	DR	CR	Balance	

Chapter 7

INVENTORY AND FINANCIAL REPORTING

LEARNING OUTCOMES

1. Define a merchandising business
2. Differentiate between the perpetual and the periodic inventory systems
3. Record inventory journal entries
4. Differentiate between single-step and multistep income statements
5. Describe the purposes and benefits of the Uniform Systems of Accounts for the Lodging Industry (USALI)
6. Prepare a summary operating statement
7. Utilize financial ratios and operating metrics to assess the performance of a profit centre

AMEENGAGE™ *Access **ameengage.com** for integrated resources including tutorials, practice exercises, the digital textbook and more.*

Assessment Questions

AS-1 (5)

What is USALI? How did it originate?

____

____

____

____

____

AS-2 (4)

What is the income statement used for?

____

____

____

____

____

____

AS-3 (❻)

What is a profit centre?

___

___

___

AS-4 (❻)

Describe the main components of a summary operating statement.

___

___

___

___

___

___

___

___

AS-5 (❼)

What is gross profit and how is it calculated?

___

___

___

AS-6 (❻)

Define distributed expenses.

___

___

___

AS-7 (❻)

Define undistributed expenses.

AS-8 (❼)

Give examples of operating metrics in the lodging industry.

AS-9 (❶)

What is a merchandising business?

AS-10 (❶)

What is COGS or cost of sales and what type of account is it?

AS-11 (❷)

In a perpetual inventory system, how often are inventory levels updated?

____

____

AS-12 (❷)

In a periodic inventory system, how often are inventory levels updated?

____

____

AS-13 (❶)

Define inventory.

____

____

____

____

AS-14 (❷ ❹)

In a perpetual inventory system, describe the transaction(s) required to record the sale of inventory.

____

____

____

AS-15 (❹)

What is one difference between a single-step income statement and a multistep income statement?

____

____

AS-16 (❹)

What are administrative expenses?

AS-17 (❻)

In a summary operating income statement, which category do items such as rent expense and insurance expense fall under?

Application Questions Group A

AP-1A (❸)

Super Shirt Wholesalers spent $10,000 to produce 1,000 shirts as inventory. Niagara Gift Shop paid $15,000 for the 1,000 shirts from Super Shirt Wholesalers on March 15, 2016. Payment is due on April 15. Assume both companies use the perpetual inventory system.

Required

a) Prepare the journal entry or entries for Niagara Gift Shop on March 15.

JOURNAL			Page 1
Date	**Account Title and Explanation**	**Debit**	**Credit**

b) Prepare the journal entry or entries for Super Shirt Wholesalers on March 15.

JOURNAL			Page 1
Date	**Account Title and Explanation**	**Debit**	**Credit**

AP-2A (❸)

Jill's Restaurant bought $3,000 worth of food on account from a produce supplier on May 10, 2016. Prepare the journal entry to record the purchase of food.

JOURNAL			Page 1
Date	Account Title and Explanation	Debit	Credit

AP-3A (❸)

On January 12, 2016, Classy Events received a shipment of T-shirts from Promo Novelties for an event. The shirts featured the event logo and each participant was to receive a shirt. The invoice amount was $5,000. Prepare the journal entry for Classy Events to record the purchase of the T-shirts.

JOURNAL			Page 1
Date	Account Title and Explanation	Debit	Credit

AP-4A (❸)

a) Bateman Motel received a shipment of bedsheets on April 3, 2016. The value of the bedsheets was $8,000. Prepare the journal entry to record the receipt of goods by Bateman Motel, assuming payment will be made in May.

JOURNAL			Page 1
Date	Account Title and Explanation	Debit	Credit

b) Journalize the transaction for Bateman Motel when the payment is made on May 3, 2016.

JOURNAL			Page 1
Date	Account Title and Explanation	Debit	Credit

AP-5A (❸)

On May 1, 2016, Sam's Bar and Grill purchased $3,100 worth of food inventory on account. On May 3, Sam's Bar and Grill used all of the food inventory to make meals which were sold for $5,400 cash. As the bookkeeper for Sam's Bar and Grill, journalize the transactions using the perpetual inventory system.

JOURNAL			Page 1
Date	Account Title and Explanation	Debit	Credit

AP-6A (❼)

If sales revenue is $300,000 and cost of sales is $180,000, what is the gross profit and gross profit margin?

AP-7A (❹ ❻ ❼)

Glent Health Spa prepared the following trial balance at its year-end of September 30, 2016. The company is owned by Wayne Glent.

Glent Health Spa Trial Balance September 30, 2016		
Account Titles	**DR**	**CR**
Cash	$14,600	
Accounts Receivable	6,000	
Inventory	6,600	
Prepaid Expenses	2,000	
Equipment	40,000	
Accumulated Depreciation		$2,500
Accounts Payable		8,000
Unearned Revenue		6,000
Bank Loan		9,000
Glent, Capital		38,750
Glent, Drawings	1,000	
Sales Revenue		61,750
Gain on Sale of Equipment		4,000
Cost of Sales	30,000	
Depreciation Expense	500	
Interest Expense	600	
Maintenance Expense	1,200	
Rent Expense	15,000	
Salaries Expense	12,500	
Total	**$130,000**	**$130,000**

Required

a) Prepare a multistep income statement.

b) If Glent Health Spa would like to prepare a summary operating statement, describe how depreciation expense and interest expense would appear in its summary operating statement.

c) What is Glent Health Spa's gross profit margin?

AP-8A (❹ ⑥)

A Bit of Fire operates a BBQ style restaurant. Some of its financial information is shown below for its fiscal year ended December 31, 2016.

Cost of Sales	$60,000
Depreciation Expense	10,000
Gain on Sale of Equipment	3,000
Interest Expense	500
Insurance Expense	7,000
Salaries Expense	50,000
Sales Revenue	145,000
Supplies Expense	2,000
Utilities Expense	9,000

Required

a) Create a multistep income statement for A Bit of Fire.

b) Create a classified multistep income statement for A Bit of Fire using the following information.

	Waiting	**Administrative**	**Total**
Salaries Expense	80%	20%	100%
Depreciation Expense	100%	0%	100%
Insurance Expense	75%	25%	100%
Utilities Expense	75%	25%	100%
Supplies Expense	0%	100%	100%

Analysis

Give a reason why expenses are categorized into "operating" and "non-operating" on a summary operating statement.

AP-9A (❼)

A Taste of Baloney has the following financial information. Calculate its gross profit and gross profit margin.

	2016
Revenue	$500,000
Cost of Sales	$350,000

AP-10A (7)

In an effort to increase business in 2016, Drive My Van (a company that provides van rentals) decided to discount its prices. Following is financial information from 2015 and 2016. Note that minimum wage for service workers increased in 2016. Round to two decimal places.

	2016	2015
Revenue	$1,000,000	$900,000
Payroll and related expenses	$800,000	$650,000

Required

a) Calculate labour cost margin for each year.

b) Give possible reasons as to why revenue and labour cost margin are different from one year to the next.

AP-11A (7)

Below is a table containing financial information for Clarabella Inn for the 2015 and 2016 fiscal year. Use the information in the table to answer the following questions. Note that in 2016, Clarabella Inn entered into an agreement with an online service company that allows travellers to book vacant rooms at Clarabella Inn at a discounted price.

Required

a) Calculate the Occupancy Rate (Note: Occupancy Rate = Nights booked ÷ Total nights available)
b) Calculate the Revenue per Available Room (Note: Revenue per Available Room = Room rental revenue ÷ Total nights available)
c) Calculate the Average Daily Rate (Note: Average Daily Rate = Room rental revenue ÷ Nights booked)

	2016	**2015**
Room rental revenue	$3,000,000	$2,800,000
Number of rooms available for rent	100	100
Number of nights in the year	365	365
Total nights available (# of rooms x # of nights in the year)	36,500	36,500
Nights booked	25,550	22,995
a) Occupancy Rate		
b) Revenue per Available Room		
c) Average Daily Rate		

d) Comment on the change in Average Daily Rate and give a possible reason for this change.

AP-12A (6)

Michelle MyGel is a beauty salon that provides hair and nail services. Hair services and nail services are provided by two separate profit centres. Michelle MyGel is a sole proprietorship, thus the company is not responsible for paying income taxes. Michelle Mignon, the owner of the salon, does all of the administrative work and does not deduct payroll for herself. Payroll expenses are paid only to the employees that Michelle hires to work in the hair and nails departments. Michelle MyGel incurred the following revenue and expenses for the year ending December 31, 2016.

Cost of sales	
Hair supplies	$10,000
Nail supplies	$7,000

Other Expenses	
Administrative	$2,000
Phone and internet	$1,200
Advertising	$500
Repair and maintenance	$600
Utilities	$1,000
Payroll—hair employees	$25,000
Payroll—nail employees	$15,000
Rent	$2,000
Property taxes	$2,000
Insurance	$3,000
Interest	$800
Depreciation	$2,000

Revenue	
Hair revenue	$50,000
Nail revenue	$30,000

Required

Arrange the above financial information for Michelle MyGel into a summary operating statement for the year ending December 31, 2016.

Application Questions Group B

AP-1B (❸)

On September 1, 2016, Fruity Crepes purchased $3,820 worth of food inventory on account. On September 4, Fruity Crepes used all of the food inventory to make cash sales of $5,920. As the bookkeeper for Fruity Crepes, journalize the transactions under the perpetual inventory system.

JOURNAL			Page 1
Date	Account Title and Explanation	Debit	Credit

AP-2B (❸)

Top Hat Grill bought $2,140 worth of food inventory on account from a produce supplier on December 8, 2016. Prepare the journal entry to record the purchase using the perpetual inventory system.

JOURNAL			Page 1
Date	Account Title and Explanation	Debit	Credit

AP-3B (❸)

a) Sleep Easy Motel received a shipment of towels on February 15, 2016. The value of the towels was $9,000. Prepare the journal entry, using the perpetual inventory system, to record the receipt of goods by Sleep Easy Motel assuming the payments for the inventory will be made in March.

JOURNAL			Page 1
Date	**Account Title and Explanation**	**Debit**	**Credit**

b) Journalize the transaction for Sleep Easy Motel when the payment is made on March 15.

JOURNAL			Page 1
Date	**Account Title and Explanation**	**Debit**	**Credit**

AP-4B (❸)

At the end of March 20, 2016, the souvenir shop at Tower Mountain received a shipment of gift mugs for resale from Cup Makers in the amount of $5,000. The invoice will be paid at a later date. Under a perpetual inventory system, journalize the following transactions.

Required

a) As the bookkeeper for Tower Mountain, record the purchase of inventory.

JOURNAL			Page 1
Date	**Account Title and Explanation**	**Debit**	**Credit**

b) Journalize the entry if payment is made on May 20.

JOURNAL			Page 1
Date	Account Title and Explanation	Debit	Credit

AP-5B (❼)

If sales are $290,000 and cost of goods sold is $130,000, what is the gross profit and gross profit margin?

AP-6B (❹)

Pakery is a shop that sells different types of pies. The following information is available for the year ending June 30, 2016.

Sales Revenue	$49,000
Maintenance Expense	800
Rent Expense	3,000
Salaries Expense	38,000
Cost of Sales	11,200
Interest Expense	1,000

Prepare the multistep income statement for June 2016.

Analysis

Pakery sold 3,500 pies at an average price of $14 each during the year. The company buys ingredients that cost $3.20 for each pie. If Pakery had sold 4,000 pies instead, would it have a positive net income? Assume operating expenses would remain the same. Show your work.

AP-7B (❹ ❼)

Wasaga Restaurant runs a family restaurant in a tourist town and also owns a banquet hall used for weddings and corporate events. Peter has prepared the income statement and balance sheet for Wasaga Restaurant as shown below.

Wasaga Restaurant Income Statement For the Year Ended December 31, 2016		
Revenues		
Sales Revenue		$975,000
Interest Revenue		25,000
Total Revenue		$1,000,000
Expenses		
Cost of Sales	350,000	
Salaries Expense	85,000	
Rent Expense	55,800	
Insurance Expense	250,200	
Loss on Property Damage	59,000	
Total Expenses		800,000
Net Income		$200,000

Required

Prepare the multistep income statement for Wasaga Restaurant.

Analysis

Calculate and interpret the gross profit margin for Wasaga Restaurant.

AP-8B (❹)

Banff Gifts is a souvenir store in a tourist town. The store's building contains a large selling area with merchandise displays and shelves, and a smaller back office area where administrative tasks such as payroll, marketing, and HR are performed. The following information is available:

- Salaries for the back office workers amounted to $80,000 for the year.
- The office area is allocated 20% of the utility and insurance costs.
- Depreciation is charged on the merchandise displayers only.

Required

Prepare a classified multistep income statement for Banff Gifts.

Banff Gifts Income Statement For the Year Ended December 31, 2016		
Sales Revenue		$1,400,000
Expenses		
Cost of Sales	$890,000	
Salaries Expense	210,000	
Office Supplies Expense	12,000	
Insurance Expense	42,000	
Utilities Expense	7,000	
Depreciation Expense	5,000	
Total Expenses		1,166,000
Net Income		$234,000

Analysis

Give a reason why it is useful to separate expenses into selling and administrative categories on the income statement.

AP-9B (❼)

Use the following financial information from Lovely Pita to calculate its gross profit and gross profit margin for 2015 and 2016. Round to two decimal places.

	2016	2015
Cost of Sales	$133,000	$140,000
Cash	$20,000	$21,000
Accounts Receivable	$35,000	$45,000
Revenue	$200,000	$235,000
Operating Expenses	$40,000	$29,000
Net Profit	$27,000	$91,000

AP-10B (❼)

Blue Jay Wei Travel Agency is a profit centre within a large tourism company. The following is the financial information for the agency for 2015 and 2016. Review the table and answer the related questions.

	2016	2015
Tour Revenue	$600,000	$700,000
Distributed Operating Expenses		
Payroll and Related Expenses	$157,000	$250,000
Booking Fees	$43,000	$50,000

a) Calculate the departmental income and departmental income margin for 2015 and 2016. Round to two decimal places.

b) Comment on the change in departmental income and departmental income margin from 2015 to 2016.

c) Calculate booking fees as a percentage of tour revenue for 2015 and 2016 and comment on the change, if any. In addition, calculate labour cost margin for 2015 and 2016 and comment on the change, if any. Use this information to give a possible reason for the change in departmental income margin from 2015 to 2016.

AP-11B (❼)

Cayenne Stepper is the department manager of a restaurant that is part of a larger organization that includes a mini-putt course and a movie theatre. The restaurant has two waiters and had 20,000 orders in 2016. Below, you will find the operating revenue and distributed operating expenses portion of the restaurant's summary operating statement for the year ending December 31, 2016.

Distributed Operating Portion of Summary Operating Statement for Cayenne's Restaurant For the Year Ended December 31, 2016	
Revenues	$415,000
Cost of Sales	$235,000
Gross Profit	$180,000
Operating Expenses (Department Specific)	
Payroll and Related Expenses	$80,000
Other Expenses	$4,000
Total Operating Expenses	$84,000
Departmental Income	$96,000

Required

a) Calculate gross profit per waiter.

b) Calculate number of orders per waiter.

c) Calculate average sales per order.

d) Calculate gross profit per order.

AP-12B (6)

Jill's Restaurant operates two profit centres. The first profit centre, restaurant, sells 200 flavours of chicken wings. The second profit centre, souvenir, sells T-shirts and caps with the restaurant logo on them. Jill's Restaurant is a sole proprietorship, thus the company is not responsible for paying income taxes. Jill Hardlock, the owner of the restaurant, does all of the administrative work and does not deduct payroll for herself. Payroll expenses are paid only to the employees that Jill hires to work in the restaurant and souvenir departments. Jill Hardlock incurred the following revenue and expenses for the year ending December 31, 2016.

Cost of sales	
Food and beverages	$500,000
Shirts and caps	$25,000

Other Expenses	
Administrative	$30,000
Phone and internet	$12,000
Advertising	$150,000
Repair and maintenance	$50,000
Utilities	$40,000
Payroll—restaurant employees	$200,000
Payroll—souvenir employees	$9,000
Rent	$10,000
Property taxes	$60,000
Insurance	$15,000
Interest	$16,000
Depreciation	$33,000

Revenue	
Restaurant revenue	$1,500,000
Souvenir revenue	$50,000

Required

Arrange the above financial information for Jill's Restaurant into a summary operating statement for the year ending December 31, 2016.

Case Study

CS-1 (❸ ❺ ❻ ❼)

Deun Hotel is a small but luxurious hotel on the west coast of Canada. It has the following three profit centres: room, restaurant and spa.

The room department manages a total of 30 rooms that are available for rent to tourists. The total number of nights booked for the years 2015 and 2016 are 7,600 and 7,900 respectively.

The restaurant department serves upscale western food, alcoholic and non-alcoholic beverages. It had three waiters in 2015, and four waiters 2016. The total numbers of orders for 2015 and 2016 were 20,000 and 28,000 respectively.

The spa department provides such services as massage, facial, manicure, pedicure and body scrub. It also sells limited skin and nail products.

Comparative summary operating statements for the years 2015 and 2016 are shown below.

Deun Hotel
Summary Operating Statement
For the Years Ended December 31, 2016 and 2015

	2016	2015
Operating Revenue		
Rooms—Revenue	$1,600,000	$1,500,000
Payroll and related expenses	300,000	250,000
Other expenses	320,000	310,000
Departmental income	980,000	940,000
Food and Beverage—Revenue	1,200,000	980,000
Cost of Sales	$200,000	150,000
Payroll and related expenses	390,000	300,000
Other expenses	194,000	150,000
Departmental income	416,000	380,000
Spa—Revenue	209,000	300,000
Cost of Sales	50,000	90,000
Payroll and related expenses	48,500	75,000
Other expenses	35,000	50,000
Departmental income	75,500	85,000
Operating Department Totals	1,471,500	1,405,000
Undistributed Operating Expenses		
Administrative and General	240,000	200,000
Information and Telecommunications Systems	80,000	60,000
Sales and Marketing	200,000	180,000
Property Operations and Maintenance	140,000	120,000
Utilities	100,000	90,000
Total Undistributed Expenses	(760,000)	(650,000)
Gross Operating Profit (GOP)	711,500	755,000
Non-Operating Income and Expenses		
Income	6,000	3,000
Rent	(35,500)	(30,000)
Property and Other Taxes	(122,000)	(111,000)
Insurance	(62,000)	(55,000)
Total Non-Operating Income and Expenses	(213,500)	(193,000)
Earnings Before Interest, Taxes, Depreciation and Amortization (EBITDA)	498,000	562,000
Less:		
Interest	55,000	50,000
Depreciation	71,000	70,000
Amortization	22,000	20,000
Total Interest, Depreciation and Amortization	(148,000)	(140,000)
Income Before Income Taxes	350,000	422,000
Income Taxes	105,000	126,600
Net Income	$245,000	$295,400

Required

a) Discuss the benefits that Deun Hotel may receive from preparing the summary operating statement under USALI.

b) You are asked to provide suggestions to Deun Hotel's senior management team on the following decisions. For each of the four decisions, suggest what you believe would be the best course of action for the upcoming year based on all of the given information, including the hotel's 2016 and 2015 performance. Support your answers with relevant numbers, financial ratios and operating metrics.

   i) Deun Hotel's management would like to increase the daily hotel room rate in order to increase profit further. According to a hospitality industry report, other luxurious hotels in the same area charge $220 per night on average. Should the room department increase its prices?

ii) Due to the high demand in the labour market for registered massage therapists, there is currently high employee turnover in the spa department. This is a major problem that requires constant management attention. Recently, there is increasing competition from cheaper spas that sell their services through various group deal sites, reducing the number of clients. Should the hotel drop the spa department entirely?

iii) Even though the restaurant department's revenue increased by $220,000 in 2016 compared to 2015, the departmental income increased by only $36,000. Should the prices of food and beverages be increased to improve the restaurant's departmental income? According to an industry report, customers spend an average of $40 per meal at other similar restaurants in the vicinity.

iv) The senior management would like to award bonuses to the manager of each profit centre based on each manager's performance in 2016. Which number in the summary operating statement should be used to evaluate the performance of each profit centre's manager?

c) On January 2, 2017, the spa department purchased $1,000 worth of skin care products inventory on account. On January 17, it sold $150 of its skin care products inventory to a client for $260 cash. On February 2, the spa department paid the supplier for the amount owed in full. Journalize these transactions under the perpetual inventory system.

Chapter 8

MANAGING ACCOUNTING INFORMATION

LEARNING OUTCOMES

1. Explain the shareholders' equity section of a corporation's balance sheet
2. Explain the key items in a corporation's income statement that are different from those in a sole proprietorship's income statement
3. Analyze the cash flow statement by interpreting the three sources and uses of cash
4. Describe payroll accounting
5. Calculate gross pay and net pay
6. Describe payroll liabilities, employer's contributions and payroll payments

AMEENGAGE *Access **ameengage.com** for integrated resources including tutorials, practice exercises, the digital textbook and more.*

Assessment Questions

AS-1 (1)

For the equity section of a balance sheet, describe the differences between how a corporation and a sole proprietorship would present the information.

AS-2 (1)

Describe the three primary differences between common shares and preferred shares.

AS-3 (❷)

On an income statement, what is a gain and how does a gain occur?

AS-4 (❸)

Is the cash flow statement an optional statement? Explain.

AS-5 (❸)

Identify the three ways a business can generate and use cash.

AS-6 (❸)

What does cash flow from operations represent?

AS-7 (❸)

What does cash flow from investments represent?

AS-8 (❸)

What does cash flow from financing represent?

AS-9 (❸)

What does the cash flow statement show?

AS-10 (❹)

Define gross pay.

AS-11 (❹)

What is net pay?

AS-12 (❻)

Define statutory deductions, and identify three statutory deductions in Canada.

AS-13 (❻)

Define voluntary deductions, and provide three examples of voluntary deductions.

AS-14 (❻)

True or False: There is no maximum amount for the Canada Pension Plan (CPP) deductions, so employees will contribute to the CPP no matter how much they earn in a year.

____

____

AS-15 (❻)

How much must an employer contribute to CPP on behalf of its employees?

____

____

AS-16 (❻)

Is there any limitation to the amount of Employment Insurance (EI) that will be deducted from an employee's pay (i.e. age, exemption amounts or maximum deductions)?

____

____

____

AS-17 (❻)

How much must the employer contribute to EI on behalf of its employees?

____

____

AS-18 (❻)

Is there any limitation to the amount of income tax that will be deducted from an employee's pay (i.e. age or maximum amounts)?

____

____

____

AS-19 (❻)

True or False: The total cost of paying an employee is equal to the amount of gross pay the employee earns.

Application Questions Group A

AP-1A (❸)

Indicate the section of the cash flow statement where each item would be located (operations, investing or financing).

Item	Section
Net Income	
Increase in Accounts Payable	
Decrease in Accounts Receivable	
Purchase of Equipment	
Payment of Bank Loan	
Increase in Inventory	
Pay Dividends	
Increase in Prepaid Insurance	

AP-2A (❸)

Bonus Airline had the following amounts in its cash flow statement for the year ended December 31, 2016.

Net decrease in cash from operations	$100,000
Net decrease in cash from investment	400,000
Net increase in cash from financing	350,000
Cash balance, January 1, 2016	600,000

Required

Calculate the cash balance at December 31, 2016

AP-3A (❸)

Mark Mortton Motel had the following totals in its cash flow statement for the year ended October 31, 2016.

Net increase from investment	$250,000
Net decrease from operations	120,000
Net increase from financing	330,000
Cash balance, November 1, 2015	65,000

Required

Calculate the net increase (decrease) in the cash balance at October 31, 2016.

____

____

____

____

____

AP-4A (❻)

Identify the following payroll deductions and expenses as statutory or voluntary, based on legislation.

Description	Statutory	Voluntary
Income taxes		
Dental benefits		
Union dues		
Savings bond purchase		
Uniform allowance		
Tuition		
Canada Pension Plan		
Prescription coverage		
Retirement deduction		
Employment Insurance		
Long-term disability		
Professional dues		
Charitable donations		
Tools and safety apparel		

AP-5A (❺)

The records of Dipsum Soft Drinks show the following figures.

Employee Earnings	
Salaries for the month	?
Overtime Pay	2,200
Total Gross Pay	?
Deductions and Net Pay	
Withheld Statutory Deductions	3,000
Charitable Contributions	?
Medical Insurance	150
Total Deductions	3,250
Net Pay	5,650

Required

Calculate the missing amounts.

____

____

____

AP-6A (❺)

Phineas Company has two employees who are paid on an hourly basis every week. Payroll information for the week ending June 26, 2015 is listed below. Overtime is paid on hours over 48 hours per week.

Employee	Hours	Hourly Rate	Income Tax	CPP	EI
H. Farnsworth	37	$16.25	$120.25	$26.43	$11.30
P. Fry	42	19.00	155.80	35.23	14.65

Calculate the gross pay and net pay for each employee.

Employee	Gross Pay	Net Pay
H. Farnsworth		
P. Fry		

AP-7A (❺ ❻)

An employer has calculated the following amounts for an employee during the last week of January 2015.

Gross wages	$1,500
Income taxes	331
Canada Pension Plan	71
Employment Insurance	28

Required

a) Calculate the employee's net pay.

____

____

b) Assuming the employer's contribution is 100% for Canada Pension Plan and 140% for Employment Insurance, what is the employer's total expense?

____

____

AP-8A (❺ ❻)

The payroll records of Russon Restaurant's district office provided the following information for the weekly pay period ended December 31, 2015.

Employee	Hours worked	Hourly Rate	Income Tax	Canada Pension Plan	Employment Insurance	Dues
Clay York	43 hrs	$12	$61	$23	$10	$10
Karen Cooper	46 hrs	15	101	33	14	10
Stephen James	48 hrs	17	134	40	17	10
Jessie Moore	40 hrs	14	66	24	11	10

Note

All employees are paid 1.5 times their hourly wage for hours worked in excess of 40 hours per week. The company contributes 100% for its share of pension plan and 140% of employment insurance.

Required

Calculate gross and net pay for each employee. Round all answers to the nearest whole number.

Employee	Gross Pay	Income Tax	Canada Pension Plan	Employ-ment Insurance	Dues	Net Pay	Employer's Cost: Canada Pension Plan	Employer's Cost: Employment Insurance
Clay York								
Karen Cooper								
Stephen James								
Jessie Moore								
Total								

AP-9A (❺ ❻)

An employee has the following information for her pay for the week ending September 25, 2015. Her employer contributes 100% towards the pension plan and 140% towards employment insurance.

Hours	38
Hourly Rate	$16.50
Income Tax	$100.32
Canada Pension Plan	$27.70
Employment Insurance	$11.79
Union Dues	$20.00
Charity Donations	$5.00

Required

a) Calculate the employee's net pay.

b) Calculate the employer's total expense.

AP-10A (❺ ❻)

Sampson Travel Agency has three employees who are paid on an hourly basis, plus time and one half for hours in excess of 44 hours per week. Payroll information for the week ending August 14, 2015 is listed below.

Employee	Hours	Hourly Rate	Income Tax	CPP	EI	Union Dues
A. Knopf	41	$14.25	$116.85	$25.59	$10.98	$10
B. Penguin	48	16.00	160.00	36.27	15.04	10
D. House	38	15.75	119.70	26.29	11.25	10

Required

Calculate the gross pay for each employee and the amount the employer will have to pay for CPP and EI.

Employee	Gross Pay	Employer CPP	Employer EI
A. Knopf			
B. Penguin			
D. House			
Total			

AP-11A (5 6)

Tremolo Tourism has three employees who work on an hourly basis and are paid bi-weekly. Each employee works 80 hours bi-weekly and overtime hours are paid at 1.5 times the regular hourly rate. Each employee contributes a portion of their pay to the United Way. The employer pays the entire amount of the health care premium for the employees. Assume the employer contributes 100% toward CPP and 140% toward EI. Payroll information for the two weeks ending August 20, 2015 is listed below.

Employee	Total Hours	Hourly Rate	Income Tax	CPP	EI	United Way	Health Care
Sing Ing	85	$12.50	$196.88	$47.48	$20.56	$5.00	$14.00
Roc N. Role	78	14.00	196.56	47.39	20.53	7.00	20.00
Hip Hopp	75	13.50	182.25	43.46	19.04	4.00	17.00

Required

a) Calculate gross and net pay for each employee.

Employee	Gross Pay	Net Pay
Sing Ing		
Roc N. Role		
Hip Hopp		
Total		

b) Calculate the employer contributions.

Employer Contributions	CPP	EI	Health Care
Sing Ing			
Roc N. Role			
Hip Hopp			
Total			

Application Questions Group B

AP-1B (❸)

Indicate the section of the cash flow statement where each item would be located (operations, investing or financing).

Item	Section
Change in Accounts Payable	
Change in Inventory	
Change in Equipment	
Change in Long-term portion of Bank Loan	
Change in Short-term portion of Bank Loan	
Change in Prepaid Rent	
Change in Accounts Receivable	
Change in Common Shares	

AP-2B (❸)

The Great Life Fitness' cash account decreased by $14,000 and its short-term investment account increased by $18,000. Cash increase from operations was $21,000. Net cash decrease from investments was $22,000.

Required

Based on the above information, calculate the cash increase (or decrease) from financing.

AP-3B (❸)

Brothers Christoph and Wilson Adler are the owners of Adler Bros Catering. They had the following totals in their cash flow statement for the year ended February 29, 2016.

Net increase from financing	$560,000
Net increase from operations	112,000
Net decrease from investment	400,000
Cash balance, March 1, 2015	88,000

Required

Calculate the net increase (decrease) in the cash balance at February 29, 2016.

AP-4B (❺ ❻)

ABC Spa showed the following information relating to employees' salaries for the month.

Gross wages	$4,300
Income taxes	739
Canada Pension Plan contributions	198
Employment Insurance contributions	81

Note: the company matches 100% of employees' pension and 140% of employees' employment insurance.

Required

a) Calculate the company's total expense.

b) Calculate the employee's net pay.

AP-5B (❺)

Hurley Johnson works as a janitor in an inn and earns $11.00 per hour. Johnson's payroll deductions include withheld income tax of $129 Canada Pension Plan of $77, Employment Insurance amounting to $35, and a monthly deduction of $40 for a charitable contribution.

Required

Calculate Hurley Johnson's gross pay and net pay assuming he worked 168 hours during the month. Round to the nearest whole dollar.

AP-6B (❺)

Sigma Five Bakery has two employees who are paid on an hourly basis every week. Payroll information for the week ending July 31, 2015 is listed below. Overtime is paid on hours over 48 hours per week.

Employee	Hours	Hourly Rate	Income Tax	CPP	EI
K. Bill	39	$22.50	$175.50	$40.10	$16.50
Q. Tarantino	43	24.00	204.00	47.16	19.18

Calculate the gross pay and net pay for each employee.

Employee	Gross Pay	Net Pay
K. Bill		
Q. Tarantino		

AP-7B (❺ ❻)

An employer has calculated the following amounts for an employee during the last week of February 2015.

Gross wages	$1,800
Income taxes	445
Canada Pension Plan	86
Employment Insurance	34

Required

a) Calculate the employee's net pay.

b) Assuming the employer's contribution is 100% for Pension Plan and 140% for Employment Insurance, what is the employer's total expense?

AP-8B (❺ ❻)

FoodsRus Company has four employees who are paid on an hourly basis, plus time and one half for hours in excess of 40 hours per week. Assume the employer contributes 100% towards the pension plan and 140% towards employment insurance. Payroll information for the week ending June 15, 2015 is listed below.

Employee	Total Hours	Hourly Rate	Income Tax	CPP	EI	Union Dues
A. Bee	40	$9.50	$26.00	$15.48	$7.14	$25.00
E. Fields	47	11.00	64.85	24.17	10.44	0.00
L. Parsons	42	11.75	55.15	21.68	9.50	15.00
I. Jay	44	10.50	51.45	20.58	9.08	15.00

Required

a) Calculate gross and net pay for each employee.

Payroll Register							
		Deductions					
Employee	Gross*	Income Tax	CPP	EI	Union Dues	Total Deductions	Net Pay
A. Bee							
E. Fields							
L. Parsons							
I. Jay							
Total							

*Remember to calculate time and one half for overtime hours.

b) Calculate the employer contributions.

Employer Contributions	
CPP	
EI	

AP-9B (❺ ❻)

An employee has the following information for his pay for the week ending April 24, 2015. His employer contributes 100% towards the pension plan and 140% towards employment insurance. Any hours worked over 40 per week is paid overtime at 1.5 times the hourly rate.

Hours	44
Hourly Rate	$18.00
Income Tax	$126.72
Canada Pension Plan	$35.87
Employment Insurance	$14.89

Required

a) Calculate the employee's net pay.

b) Calculate the employer's total expense.

AP-10B (❺ ❻)

Ridell Resort has two employees who are paid on an hourly basis, plus time and one half for hours in excess of 44 hours per week. Payroll information for the week ending May 29, 2015 is listed below.

Employee	Hours	Hourly Rate	Income Tax	CPP	EI
D. Troi	38	$15.25	$115.90	$25.35	$10.89
W. Crusher	50	18.00	190.80	43.89	17.94

Required

Calculate the gross pay for each employee and the amount the employer will have to pay for CPP and EI.

Employee	Gross Pay	Employer CPP	Employer EI
D. Troi			
W. Crusher			
Total			

AP-11B (❹ ❺ ❻)

Rippling Waters rents canoes and other watercraft to campers and hikers. On May 15, 2015, Rippling Waters prepared its semi-monthly payroll for employees. The employer pays half of the health care premium, and the employees pay the other half. Assume the employer contributes 100% toward the pension plan and 140% toward employment insurance. Payroll information for May 15, 2015 is listed below.

Employee	Total Hours	Hourly Rate	Income Tax	CPP	EI	Health Care
M. Swift	87.5	$14.50	$253.75	$55.58	$23.85	$18.00
S. Current	85.5	15.00	256.50	56.27	24.11	20.00
B. Wavey	73.5	13.50	198.45	41.90	18.65	14.00

Required

a) Calculate gross and net pay for each employee:

Employee	Gross Pay	Net Pay
M. Swift		
S. Current		
B. Wavey		
Total		

b) Calculate the employer contributions:

Employer Contributions	CPP	EI	Health Care
M. Swift			
S. Current			
B. Wavey			
Total			

Case Study

CS-1 (❶❷❸)

After learning that you're taking an accounting course, Kim, your close friend, has come to ask you for investment advice. She went skiing at Whistler Blackcomb last winter and was so impressed by the resort that she has been thinking about investing in it. Because she doesn't know how to read financial statements, she asked you to analyze Whistler Blackcomb's financial statements and comment on the company's financial performance. The statements are presented below.

Whistler Blackcomb Consolidated Balance Sheet (in thousands) As at September 30, 2014 and 2013		
	2014	**2013**
Assets		
Cash	$ 8,410	$ 41,353
Short-term Investments	145	311
Accounts receivable	4,496	3,323
Inventories	18,633	15,856
Prepaid expenses	3,985	2,727
Total Current Assets	**35,669**	**63,570**
Notes receivable	777	2,636
Property, buildings and equipment	319,897	322,316
Property held for development	9,244	9,244
Intangible assets	300,778	311,428
Goodwill	137,354	137,259
Total Assets	**$ 803,719**	**$ 846,453**
Liabilities		
Accounts payable and accrued liabilities	25,715	24,927
Income taxes payable	2,403	1,645
Provisions	2,139	2,858
Deferred revenue	27,610	22,347
Total Current Liabilities	**57,867**	**51,777**
Long-term debt	229,855	258,042
Deferred income tax liability	21,974	20,690
Limited partner's interest	72,796	72,796
Total Liabilities	**382,492**	**403,305**
Shareholders' Equity		
Common shares	495,176	497,929
Retained earnings (deficit)	(73,949)	(54,781)
Shareholders' Equity	**421,227**	**443,148**
Liabilities and Shareholders' Equity	**$ 803,719**	**$ 846,453**

Whistler Blackcomb Consolidated Income Statement (in thousands) For the Years Ended September 30, 2014 and 2013		
	2014	**2013**
Resort revenue	$ 254,517	$ 240,780
Operating expenses	134,081	126,673
Depreciation and amortization	41,254	40,249
Selling, general and administrative	27,761	27,673
Total Expenses	203,096	194,595
Operating Income Before Tax	**51,421**	**46,185**
Other income	3,068	0
Other expense	(30,712)	(25,607)
Income Before Income Tax	23,777	20,578
Income tax expense	5,737	7,248
Net Income	**$ 18,040**	**$ 13,330**

Whistler Blackcomb Summary of the Cash Flow Statement (in thousands) For the Years Ended September 30, 2014 and 2013		
	2014	**2013**
Net cash provided by operations	$ 67,848	$ 64,725
Net cash used by investing	(28,398)	(24,345)
Net cash used by financing	(72,393)	(42,661)
Net increase (decrease) in cash	$ (32,943)	$ (2,281)

Required

a) Explain to Kim what a retained earnings deficit in Whistler Blackcomb's balance sheet means.

b) According to Whistler Blackcomb's Notes to the Consolidated Financial Statements, "other expense" on the income statement includes "loss on disposal of fixed assets". Explain to Kim what "loss" means and why it's reported as "other expense" rather than "operating expenses".

c) Does the fact that Whistler Blackcomb had a net decrease in cash in both 2013 and 2014 mean that it's not a good company to invest in?